COMPUTERS AND THE HUMAN MIND

This book is D<small>ONALD</small> G. F<small>INK</small>'s second contribution to the Science Study Series; he was co-author (with David M. Lutyens) of *The Physics of Television,* published in 1960. Formerly director of research of the Philco Corporation and editor-in-chief of *Electronics* magazine, he became, in 1962, general manager of the Institute of Electrical and Electronics Engineers.

Mr. Fink was born in Englewood, New Jersey, in 1911, and was educated at the Massachusetts Institute of Technology (B.Sc., 1933) and Columbia University (M.Sc., 1942). He had been interested in radio since boyhood and at sixteen had received a license as an amateur radio operator. He joined the editorial staff of *Electronics* on his graduation from M.I.T.

In World War II Mr. Fink was an expert consultant with the Office of the Secretary of War, concerned especially with the Loran navigation system. He has represented the United States as a Department of State technical adviser at several international conferences on television. In 1958 he was president of the Institute of Radio Engineers.

Mr. Fink has written articles for technical journals, prepared material on television for *Encyclopædia Britannica* and *Collier's Encyclopedia,* and written several books besides *The Physics of Television.* Among his publications are *Radar Engineering* and *Television Engineering.*

COMPUTERS
AND
THE HUMAN MIND

by Donald G. Fink

Published by Anchor Books
Doubleday & Company, Inc.
Garden City, New York
1966

THE SCIENCE STUDY SERIES

The Science Study Series offers to students and to the general public the writing of distinguished authors on the most stirring and fundamental topics of physics, from the smallest known particles to the whole universe. Some of the books tell of the role of physics in the world of man, his technology and civilization. Others are biographical in nature, telling the fascinating stories of the great discoverers and their discoveries. All the authors have been selected both for expertness in the fields they discuss and for ability to communicate their special knowledge and their own views in an interesting way. The primary purpose of these books is to provide a survey of physics within the grasp of the young student or the layman. Many of the books, it is hoped, will encourage the reader to make his own investigations of natural phenomena.

These books are published as part of a fresh approach to the teaching and study of physics. At the Massachusetts Institute of Technology during 1956 a group of physicists, high school teachers, journalists, apparatus designers, film producers, and other specialists organized the Physical Science Study Committee, now operating as a part of Educational

Services Incorporated, Watertown, Massachusetts. They pooled their knowledge and experience toward the design and creation of aids to the learning of physics. Initially their effort was supported by the National Science Foundation, which has continued to aid the program. The Ford Foundation, the Fund for the Advancement of Education, and the Alfred P. Sloan Foundation have also given support. The Committee has created a textbook, an extensive film series, a laboratory guide, especially designed apparatus, and a teacher's source book.

The Series is guided by a Board of Editors, consisting of Bruce F. Kingsbury, Managing Editor; John H. Durston, General Editor; Paul F. Brandwein, the Conservation Foundation and Harcourt, Brace & World, Inc.; Samuel A. Goudsmit, Brookhaven National Laboratory; Philippe LeCorbeiller, Harvard University, and Gerard Piel, *Scientific American.*

CONTENTS

CONTENTS

COMPUTERS AND THE HUMAN MIND

CHAPTER 1

MINDS AND MACHINES

> The machine played a perfect ending without one misstep. In the matter of the end game, I have not had such competition from any human being since 1954, when I lost my last game.
>
> —ROBERT W. NEALEY

In the summer of 1962 at Yorktown Heights, New York, a former checkers champion of Connecticut, Robert W. Nealey, lost a game of checkers for the first time in eight years. His opponent, a comparative newcomer to the game, had first learned to play in 1955 and had picked up the fine points of the game rapidly. Mr. Nealey was concerned, understandably, to be defeated by a tyro—and it was not consoling that his conqueror should be a machine, an IBM Model 7094 electronic computer. The automaton won fairly and squarely, without coaching from the sidelines. Moreover, it had learned to play as a human being learns, from experience and observation, recognizing mistakes and remembering not to repeat them.

An expert at checkers watching the game would have been confident that the machine displayed highly developed intelligence. The play showed that the machine was "looking ahead" as many as twenty moves and was employing strategy worthy of a champion, as its victory clearly demonstrated. Most remarkable was the fact that the man who devised the checker-playing routine for the computer, Dr. Arthur L. Samuel, was not himself a noted player. He did not, and indeed could not, plan the particular strategy that defeated champion Nealey. So far as outward appearances were concerned, the machine seemed to have "a mind of its own." Of course, the machine was not intelligent in the human sense. But in the special world of championship checkers it behaved as if it possessed a highly trained mind.

Actually, the computer was doing only what it was designed to do—arithmetic, and a particularly simple-minded arithmetic at that. It added, subtracted, shifted, compared, and remembered numbers composed of just two digits, 0 and 1. It manipulated these numbers in accordance with a master plan based on the rules of checkers. Later in this book we shall see how a computer can make judgments in a game and decide its next move, how it learns from experience. For the present, we need only note that the machine *did* beat a champion at his own game, by following a computation devised to imitate the behavior of the human mind.

Learning from Experience

Why should a machine play checkers at all? Using a large and expensive computer to play checkers might be dismissed as a "stunt," of no lasting significance to science or technology. But Dr. Samuel's purpose was more profound than merely to put IBM 7094 against Mr. Nealey. He adopted checkers as an example of an intellectual pursuit, with well-defined and not too complicated rules that could be reduced to computer science. His objective was to demonstrate methods by which a machine can be made to learn from experience.

When the 7094 computer first was set up to play checkers, it was arranged to make only the elementary moves. The machine was a raw beginner, and even a child could beat it. But the machine was programmed to store away, on magnetic tape, the sequences of play resulting in capture of the opponent's men and invasion of the opponent's king row. Since a single roll of computer tape can store many millions of digits, the machine was able to remember a prodigious number of patterns of play. In deciding on its next move the computer compared the existing pattern of play with many patterns it had stored away, and it chose a move that its experience had showed would lead, most probably, to the discomfiture of the opponent.

As the machine continued to play, its store of experience grew. It became able to produce and store more general patterns of play, the tactics of keeping control of the board, and of protecting the king row. The day came, in fact, after several thousand games, when the IBM 7094 machine could consistently defeat Dr. Samuel, who rates himself a "fair amateur" at the game. At that stage the machine's store of checker lore, for particular moves as well as for general strategy, had outgrown the mental capacity of the man who taught it!

Playing games with champions is a dramatic example of apparently intelligent behavior by a computer, but it is only one of many different forms of machine intelligence. Computers have been programmed to translate languages, to read addresses on envelopes and to sort them by city and state, to prove mathematical theorems, to set type for newspapers (including the difficult task of hyphenation), to design in days a complicated electronic system that would take months of human brain power—all without human intervention. In these seemingly fantastic accomplishments, there is no mystery at all, once you understand how a computer works and how the computation plan can be made to imitate logical processes. Planning such computation takes much tedious work, for at every stage of the fabulously intricate process there must be an instruction or set of instructions that originated in a human mind.

Why then rent a computer, at several hundred dollars per hour, to do these jobs? If the programmer must understand the problem, why not solve it himself? The answer lies in the demands of money and time. The computer can perform many "intellectual" tasks more accurately and more cheaply and much, much faster than human beings can perform them. The large electronic computer of today can process numerical information about a million times as fast as a man. Being a machine, it can work long hours without fatigue and without making mistakes. The computer's ability to store and recall masses of detailed information is far ahead of the best performance of human memory. It can store within itself, in tiny magnetic cores or films,

4

hundreds of thousands of digits and recall any one of them in less than a millionth of a second. With such vastly superhuman resources of speed, accuracy, endurance, and memory at his command, the computer scientist can devise computations of such grand scope that they can, in fact, imitate many forms of human thought.

The machine's ability to imitate human intelligence is limited, of course, in many ways, for the mind of man, as we shall see in Chapter 9, is a marvelously versatile organ. A computer can solve a variety of problems in arithmetic, geometry, or trigonometry, or find approximate solutions of very difficult differential equations, but its computation plan must be set up to solve just one type of problem at a time. The program of computation must be changed whenever a new type is presented. On versatility the computer lags far behind.

The computer is limited also to those types of intellectual effort that can be reduced to a scheme of computation. The fact that such mental activities as reading, translating, problem solving, and playing games can be reduced to numerical manipulation comes as a surprise to almost everyone not familiar with computer technology. The explanation is simple: whether we are conscious of the fact or not, the brain employs the rules of logic. In a very real sense, the brain *is* a computer and its computer-like functions can be imitated by machinery.

Computers can perform many intellectual tasks, particularly repetitive and tedious tasks, in a few minutes that would take far more than a lifetime of human effort. Since highly trained brain power is a commodity in short supply, computer systems increasingly will take over such mental chores. Just as the engines of electricity and internal combustion have changed radically the ways in which we use our muscles, the intelligent machine will change the ways in which we use our brains.

This prospect has altered the outlook for every young person who is planning a career in science or technology. It will affect, less directly, careers in politics or business, law or medicine. We must not conclude, however, that intelligent machinery will take over so completely that professional people will be put out of work. Precisely the reverse is true. The automobile, for example, has greatly increased our range of travel. So also will the intellectual engine greatly increase the range of the trained mind. The automobile and the computer system illustrate, in fact, one of the most significant trends in modern society, the steady change from direct *action* toward indirect *control*.

The automobile transfers the problem of locomotion from muscles to nervous system, with physical effort reduced to a light touch on the wheel and the gas pedal. The machine does all the "real work." Similarly, the methods of artificial intelligence are transferring many types of brain work from direct labor of the mind to indirect control of machine computation. The hand on the wheel of the intelligent machine is the hand that composes the computation plan. The machine does all the "real work."

A Tool for the Scientific Method

Machine methods not only save time, which we can use creatively in other intellectual pursuits, but they also provide the means for exhaustive investigation of problems too complicated or tedious for the unaided brain. The intelligent machine is, in other words, a new tool for the scientific method. By systematic comparisons of the patterns of logic, at million-per-second speeds, computers can explore the realms of the intellect in details never before perceived.

Such explorations already are under way in many fields of science and engineering. They run the gamut from simple extensions of familiar arithmetic to complex studies of the nature of human behavior. Let us consider two examples that illustrate the extremes: (1) using a computer to figure π to 100,000 decimal places and (2) using a computer to help us to understand how we recognize a familiar scene.

The first example is a simple routine; the computer operates in a straightforward manner, fast and furiously to be sure, but without sophisticated decision-making or learning routines. The second is an attempt to imitate the mind in one of its most extraordinary accomplishments, the perception of subtle differences of form. In the second example, an intelligent machine learns to distinguish the features of photographs by repeated observation. Its success is marginal, but the results are sufficiently good (and sufficiently hard to understand) that this experiment rates as one of the most significant in the field of artificial intelligence.

100,000 Decimals for π

Consider now a computer system working on the digits represented by the + sign following the number $\pi = 3.14159265+$. The nature of this number is one of the great puzzles of mathematics, arising from the pattern shown in Fig. 1. Our intuition tells

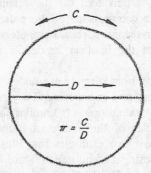

$$\pi = \frac{C}{D}$$

FIG. 1. The puzzle of π. A computer figures this unruly number to 100,000 decimal places in less than nine hours.

us that the lengths of the circumference and the diameter of a circle are equally knowable quantities. We can see them in the same glance, and we can imagine unrolling the circumference into a straight line without committing a sin against the postulates of Euclid. But, as we well know, our imagination fools us. For, if we could do this, we would have two straight lines of equally definite length, the straightened-out circumference and the diameter, and the ratio of these lines would have a definite value. But the ratio of circumference to diameter, π, is not a definite number. It is a number without end, of the special type known as transcendental; that is, it cannot be expressed by a finite collection of digits.

Faced with this unruly behavior, we conclude that

8

curved lines and straight ones cannot be compared with ultimate precision; we can express one only as an approximation of the other. The fact that the approximation can be refined to any degree we wish has not removed the puzzle of what happens when we "straighten out" a curved line.

So π has been a number to conjure with. Uncounted hours of human toil have been spent over the past two centuries in computing hundreds of its decimal digits and attempting to find some pattern in them that would prove it had a definite value. No pattern has been found and, since 1882, when the German mathematician Ferdinand von Lindemann (1852–1939) proved that π was a transcendental number, the search has been known to be fruitless.

Why, then, has π been computed to 100,000 decimal places? Not, certainly, for any practical purpose. A simple calculation shows that ten decimals are sufficient to compute the circumference of the earth to better than an inch. Simon Newcomb, the American astronomer, observed that thirty decimals of π (3.14159265358979323846264338327 9+) would suffice to specify the circumference of the visible universe to an error too small for the most powerful microscope to detect.

Perhaps the reason for the exhaustive calculation of π is simply that it is easy to accomplish with modern high-speed computers and it is, therefore, a popular exercise in computer programming. Calculation of π is also something like mountain climbing. We want to know the next decimal because "it is there," because it adds one tiny fraction to man's

9

knowledge of nature's fundamental constants. Also behind the decimal hunt is what Tobias Dantzig* terms "the forlorn hope" of discovering some sort of regularity that would throw light on the nature of π.

To program a computer to figure π is an elementary exercise now assigned to high school students lucky enough to have a computer to work with. For our purposes a useful series for π (there are several) is the following:

$$\pi = 4/1 - 4/3 + 4/5 - 4/7 + 4/9 - 4/11 + 4/13 - 4/15 + 4/17 - 4/19 + 4/21 - 4/23 + 4/25 - 4/27 + 4/29 \text{ and so on ad infinitum}$$

A computer may be arranged to calculate this series by forming fractions, whose numerators are all 4 and whose denominators are successively the odd integers, adding them with alternate changes in sign and terminating the addition at any desired point. True, this brute force approach is not used in the decimal hunt, since to find 100,000 decimal places this way would require us to add more than $10^{100,000}$ terms! There are shortcuts that must be used even with a very fast computer.

Typical shortcuts can be explored if you can borrow a desk calculator (one that divides automatically and gives eight-digit answers). An hour or two (with the help of a friend) is sufficient time to compute and add 100 terms in the series given above. The sum of the first 98 terms gives a too-low value of 3.1313888; the first 99 terms a too-high value of

* *Number, The Language of Science* (Doubleday & Company Anchor Books), p. 119.

3.1516934; 100 terms give a too-low value of 3.1315929.

The *average* of the 98-term and 99-term sums is much closer, 3.1415411 (but too low); and the average of the 99-term sum and the 100-term sum is also close, 3.1416432 (but too high). We can then take the *average of these two averages* and get an answer close enough for all ordinary calculations, 3.1415921+, whereas the correct value is 3.1415-926+. The error in this result is 0.0000005/-3.1415926 or less than two parts in ten million! This process is illustrated in Fig. 2. We shall have several occasions to return to this computation.

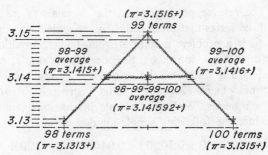

FIG. 2. A computational shortcut. By taking averages of too-small and too-large values, the approximation of π may be extended from one decimal place to six.

We thus find that simple addition of 100 terms in this series gives only one correct decimal place, while averaging of two successive sums produces three correct decimals, and averaging two successive averages can refine the result to six decimal places. Similar methods are used in machine computation.

Methods are available for massive computation of decimals, whereby the problem is broken up into segments small enough to be handled one at a time. But the main scheme is the same: form terms in a series and, by taking averages, concentrate on the small differences between successive terms. The hundred-thousand-decimal calculation took 8 hours, 43 minutes of computer time, working at an average speed of over 100,000 additions and subtractions per second. At a desk calculator, it is estimated that the same job would take 30,000 years!

Discovering a Series for π

The reverse process—given the decimals of π, to find the series that produced them—is something else, but it is a problem a computer can tackle, provided we do not ask too much. Suppose, for example, we feed into a computer the value of π correct to five decimal places (3.14159+) and instruct it to produce a series. With very simple instructions it can produce the following simple-minded answer:

$$\pi = 3.00000 + 0.10000 + 0.04000 + 0.00100 + 0.00050 + 0.00009+$$

For this result the computer has merely counted off digits, starting at the rightmost decimal place and proceeding to the left, until only zeroes remained, a completely trivial exercise, of course. It does not add one whit to the information given to the computer in the first place.

Computers can do much better. Suppose we instruct a computer to find a series for π, using theorems of geometry. We tell the computer to figure the

12

perimeters of regular polygons inscribed within and circumscribed about a circle of unit diameter, as shown in Fig. 3, using polygons with even numbers

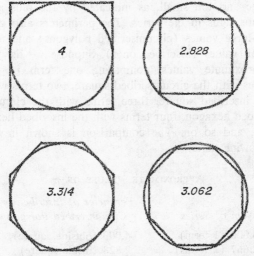

FIG. 3. Archimedes' method used inscribed and circumscribed regular polygons to bound the limits of π. Shown are the values approximated by squares and octagons. For 100-sided polygons the values are 3.1426 and 3.1411.

of sides. We supply to the computer the equations for the perimeters of inscribed and circumscribed polygons in terms of the diameter of the circle, and we program it to find the perimeters for 4, 6, 8, 10, 12 sides and so on up to, say, 100 sides. The larger the number of sides, the more nearly the perimeter matches the circumference.

We now compare these perimeters, which the

computer prints out on an electric typewriter, with the values of π obtained by our numerical series (page 10). We note, as we take more and more terms, that the series gives values alternately too large and too small, as indicated by the plus and minus signs in the series. The perimeters also give too-large values (circumscribed polygons) and too-small values (inscribed ones). Suppose we list the approximate values, comparing one term in the series with the circumscribed square, two terms with the inscribed square, three terms with the circumscribed hexagon, four terms with the inscribed hexagon, and so on. The comparison is shown in the following table:

APPROXIMATE VALUES OF π

Sum of Series	Perimeter of Inscribed or Circumscribed Polygon
4.000 (1 term)	4.000 (outside square)
2.667 (2 terms)	2.828 (inside square)
3.467 (3 terms)	3.464 (outside hexagon)
2.895 (4 terms)	3.000 (inside hexagon)
3.340 (5 terms)	3.314 (outside octagon)
3.976 (6 terms)	3.062 (inside octagon)

After the first term, we can see, the perimeters give more accurate values. Thus, in effect, the computer has arrived at a different series for π that converges more rapidly than our numerical series. At first glance, this is an elegant accomplishment. But has the computer behaved in an intelligent fashion? Of course, it has not!

To see why, let us compare the computer with Archimedes who, two hundred years before Christ, used inscribed and circumscribed polygons to find a value of π, placing it between 3-1/7 and 3-10/71.† Our computer has merely reproduced Archimedes' calculations. It has not *invented* Archimedes' creative concept of using polygons to approximate the circumference. That idea was *given* to the computer by its human operator. The computer was in no way creative.

We must leave for the last chapter of this book the question of whether computers can be creative. For now, our excursion into the computation of π has served only to show a most primitive type of investigation, based on explicit instructions. True, the computer can go further in discovering the decimals of π than man can go with simpler tools (paper and pencil, or a desk calculator). But this proves merely that the electronic computer is a superior tool; nothing really new has been added. In fact, such rote computations do not qualify for the term "artificial intelligence." This designation is reserved for machines that observe, compare, and learn.

How to Tell a Bridge from a Dam

We turn now to our second example of computer science, at the other end of the scale of machine intelligence. Here we have a machine that learns from experience, that seems to acquire an ability to recognize some features of photographs. Its performance is not sufficiently good to qualify as a replacement

† History does not record whether Archimedes considered, as a more accurate value, the number midway between his limits (3-705/4970). If he did, he arrived at the value 3.14185, which is correct to better than 1 part in 10,000!

for human observation and learning. But the fact that it works at all is not easy to understand, since the machine works without detailed instructions from its human designer and operator.

This machine, nicknamed "Whirling Dervish," is a significant example of artificial intelligence for another reason: it is one of several similar machines that have been constructed to aid man's quest for knowledge of how the human brain operates. As we shall see in a later chapter, much is known about the structure of the brain and the ways in which it responds to environment. But brain surgeons and psychologists agree that the brain is so complex an organ, and so difficult to study both inside and outside the skull, that the present body of knowledge is a small island in a sea of ignorance.

The electronic computer has been welcomed by these specialists because it is the only machine complex enough to imitate the brain. So computers are being used to test theories of brain function. One such theory is that, in recognizing its surroundings, the brain uses many millions of nerve cells. When the learning process starts, the connections between the cells are largely random. As the process proceeds, certain connections are reinforced while others are de-emphasized. A pattern of connections thus gradually builds up, and the pattern inside the brain eventually matches the pattern of observation and stimulation fed to it from the outside world.

To test this theory, we can start with a computer system whose connections are initially random, and arrange for these connections to be emphasized or de-emphasized by information fed to it from its surroundings. When the pattern of computer connections (stored magnetically in the computer memory) has been established, we then present a "test case" to the computer and ask it to determine whether its pattern matches, even approximately, the stored pattern. The computer responds with a recognition of the test object, the certainty of recognition depending on the degree of the approximation in the matching process.

The Whirling Dervish performs this task. The machine, which resembles a motion picture projector with a computer attached, looks at a photograph through a lens. In a typical experiment, an aerial photograph of a road crossing a bridge over a stream is presented to the machine. Behind the lens (Fig. 4) is a strip of motion picture film, in the form of a

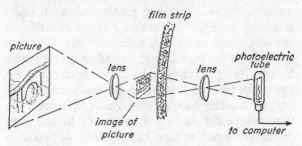

FIG. 4. The Whirling Dervish. This machine learns to recognize the contents of pictures by repeated inspection through irregular patterns on a strip of film.

closed loop. On each frame of the film has been photographed a pattern of irregularly shaped lines (Fig. 5). There are two hundred such frames and the pattern on each is entirely random, having no

|←—one frame—→|

FIG. 5. Four typical film frames used by the Whirling Dervish. Each picture is inspected through 200 such patterns.

correlation with the patterns on the other 199 frames. Behind the film is a photoelectric tube, which translates into electric current the light coming from the picture through the film frame. The current is fed, through intermediate apparatus, to a computer.

Each frame of the film is held stationary, for a moment, between lens and phototube, and the film is moved through the machine a frame at a time in motion-picture fashion. A different value of current is produced for each frame, depending on the match between the pattern of light in the picture and the pattern of lines on that frame. In one complete passage of the film two hundred values of current are thus produced,‡ and these are stored by the computer. The machine then has a pattern of two hundred observations of the picture derived by inspection through random patterns of lines. This sounds like a lot, but it merely tickles the computer memory, which can cope with millions of stored values.

‡ Actually, the electric currents stored have only two values. The numeral 1 is stored in the computer when the light passing to the phototube is above average, while the numeral 0 is stored when the light is at or below average. This circuitry permits the computer to operate directly with the binary digits for which it was designed.

We now repeat the process for nine additional aerial pictures, each of which is a road on the bridge, to the same scale but otherwise not alike. The shape of the road, the construction of the bridge, the appearance of the surrounding terrain are, in general, all different in the ten pictures. For each picture we store two hundred current values and at the conclusion of the "training sequence," the computer has stored ten patterns of two hundred digits each. The computer is then instructed to compare the ten patterns of digits to determine the ways in which they are alike and the ways in which they differ.

Class Patterns

The machine must, of course, be instructed very explicitly as to the procedure for this comparison. Actually it employs well-known methods of statistical correlation, the details of which are beyond the scope of this book. The end result is a "class pattern" of two hundred digits which embodies all the information which the computer discovers concerning the similarities and dissimilarities of the ten observations of the ten pictures. The machine has thus been "trained" by exposure to the ten pictures. As each new picture is presented it "learns" more about the class of pictures known as "roads on bridges."

The whole process is repeated with ten other pictures, each of which is a different aerial photograph of a road crossing the top of a dam. The shapes and constructions of the dams are different, so ten different patterns of two hundred digits each are derived and stored. The patterns are examined by the computer, using the same statistical correlation routine, and a second "class pattern" (which embodies the information in the ten pictures of dams) is computed and stored. Now the machine has "learned," by observation through random patterns of lines, something about pictures of a second class, "roads on dams."

Finally, we come to the crucial test. We select a picture that the machine has not seen before, of a road on a bridge, and present it to the machine. The picture is observed in the same manner, the machine producing and storing a string of two hundred digits. These digits are then compared, within the computer, with the "class patterns" previously derived. It is comparatively simple for the machine, using correlation methods, to determine whether the "test" digit pattern is more like the "bridge" class pattern or more like the "dam" class pattern. The computer, having made the comparison, prints out the answer: the test picture is "most probably" a road on a bridge. The identification, being based on statistical comparisons, is never certain, and the machine often makes mistakes. But in the case of pictures of roads it does produce correct identifications better than 80 per cent of the time.

What does this prove? First it shows that a learning process based on initially random observations is possible. The machine's performance does not prove that the brain works this way, but it shows that the brain could operate in a similar manner, and it encourages further exploration. Second, it shows that a machine can operate in an apparently "intelligent" fashion without benefit of detailed instructions provided by a human operator. The human contribution to this machine was an abstraction of high order: the machine was instructed to apply the routines of statistics to random observations, nothing more. For all the details, the machine was on its own.

No one has yet tried to follow, in logical detail, just what shapes, boundaries, and shadings the machine used in recognizing, correctly, the difference between a picture of a bridge and a picture of a dam. Some day, of course, a point-by-point analysis of the machine's decision process will be known, and then the mystery of its perception will be dispelled. Meanwhile, we can only admit that a machine can display behavior strangely imitative of human intelligence, and that it can do so with highly abstract instructions—a far cry from the explicit routines used in computing the decimals of π.

CHAPTER 2

ARITHMETIC FOR COMPUTERS

> Machines will slowly take over from men all the
> tedious thinking which yet must be done without
> error; all the sorting and checking and counting
> and repetitive calculation which, frankly, makes
> machines of us.—A. M. UTTLEY

The first thing to understand about electronic computers is that they do what they are told to do, no
more and no less. The second is that instructions to
computers must be simple and straightforward. A
computer can solve a complex problem, but only if
a human being first has broken the problem down
into a sequence of small steps. For the most part,
these steps are simple operations in the simplest
arithmetic, *binary arithmetic,* which uses only the
digits 0 and 1.

If we are to see how a computer solves complex
problems we need some familiarity with the small
steps of computer arithmetic. This chapter will review first how people can figure using only 0 and 1,
and then will show how certain simple electric circuits can perform in the same way.

From Decimal to Binary—and Back

Let us start with numbers almost everyone knows
well, numbers in decimal notation, made up of the
digits 0 through 9. In decimal notation the *position*
of each digit in a number has associated with it a
power of ten. Proceeding to the left from the decimal point, the first digit expresses the ones ($10^0 = 1$);
the second expresses the tens ($10^1 = 10$); the next
the hundreds ($10^2 = 100$), and so on. We can write
the powers of ten in words above each digit:

ten thousands	*thousands*	*hundreds*	*tens*	*ones*
1	0	2	5	6

We also can express the number 10256 as the sum
of five decimal numbers, formed by multiplying each
digit by the corresponding power of ten and adding
the products:

$$
\begin{aligned}
1 \times 10^4 &= 10000 \\
0 \times 10^3 &= 0000 \\
2 \times 10^2 &= 200 \\
5 \times 10^1 &= 50 \\
6 \times 10^0 &= 6 \\
\hline
&10256
\end{aligned}
$$

The same rules govern the formation of binary
numbers. In binary notation, each digit has associated with it a *power of 2*. The first digit to the left
of the binary point expresses units ($2^0 = 1$); the next
to the left expresses twos ($2^1 = 2$), the next fours
($2^2 = 4$), the next eights ($2^3 = 8$), and so on. The
decimal number 46, for example, can be shown in
binary as the following powers of 2:

thirty-twos	*sixteens*	*eights*	*fours*	*twos*	*ones*
1	0	1	1	1	0

or it may be understood as the sum of five binary numbers:

$$
\begin{aligned}
1 \times 2^5 &= 100000 \\
0 \times 2^4 &= 00000 \\
1 \times 2^3 &= 1000 \\
1 \times 2^2 &= 100 \\
1 \times 2^1 &= 10 \\
0 \times 2^0 &= 0 \\
\hline
&101110
\end{aligned}
$$

To convert binary numbers into decimal form, we express each product in *decimal* notation and add the decimal products: The binary number 101110 is thus converted:

$$
\begin{aligned}
1 \times 2^5 &= 32 \\
0 \times 2^4 &= 0 \\
1 \times 2^3 &= 8 \\
1 \times 2^2 &= 4 \\
1 \times 2^1 &= 2 \\
0 \times 2^0 &= 0 \\
\hline
&46
\end{aligned}
$$

That is, 101110 in binary is equal to 46 in decimal. The equality may be expressed by the notation $101110_2 = 46_{10}$, the subscripts 2 and 10 indicating that the numbers are binary and decimal, respectively.

For the reverse conversion, from decimal numbers to binary form, the decimal form must be split into the powers of 2. Divide the decimal number repeatedly by two, that is, the whole into halves, the halves into quarters, the quarters into eighths, the eighths into sixteenths, and so on. Whenever one of the successive dividends is an odd number, the quotient has a remainder of 1; even-number dividends have a remainder of 0. Each remainder in each division is a digit of the binary equivalent of the decimal number.

To find the binary equivalent of 46, for example, divide by two, producing a quotient of 23 and a remainder of 0. This remainder represents the *zero* power of 2 in 46, so it is the rightmost digit of the binary form. Then divide 23 by 2, producing a quotient of 11 with a remainder of 1. The remainder represents the *first* power of two, and it serves as the next digit, to the left, in the binary form.

The whole process of converting 46_{10} into binary form looks like this:

$$
\begin{array}{rl}
2\,)\ \ 46 & \\
2\,)\ \ 23 & \text{remainder } 0 \\
2\,)\ \ 11 & \qquad\quad\; 1 \\
2\,)\ \ \ 5 & \qquad\quad\; 1 \\
2\,)\ \ \ 2 & \qquad\quad\; 1 \\
2\,)\ \ \ 1 & \qquad\quad\; 0 \\
\ \ \ \ \ \ 0 & \qquad\quad\; 1
\end{array}
$$

We write the remainders down in order, from the bottom to the top, and find that $46_{10} = 101110_2$.

Just to make sure of the method, we will repeat the conversion from decimal to binary with another decimal, this time the number 218:

```
2 ) 218
2 ) 109      remainder 0
2 )  54          "       1
2 )  27          "       0
2 )  13          "       1
2 )   6          "       1
2 )   3          "       0
2 )   1          "       1
      0          "       1
```

Again writing down the remainders from bottom to top we have:

$$218_{10} = 11011010_2$$

We can check this conversion by working backward from the binary form to the decimal:

$$
\begin{aligned}
1 \times 2^7 &= 128 \\
1 \times 2^6 &= 64 \\
0 \times 2^5 &= 0 \\
1 \times 2^4 &= 16 \\
1 \times 2^3 &= 8 \\
0 \times 2^2 &= 0 \\
1 \times 2^1 &= 2 \\
0 \times 2^0 &= 0 \\
\hline
& 218 \quad \text{(Q.E.D.)}
\end{aligned}
$$

Evidently, converting numbers from decimal to binary and vice versa is a cumbersome exercise, for people at least, and there are many opportunities for mistakes in figuring and adding the powers of 2 and 10. Readers wanting further practice may wish to explore the problem by finding the binary equivalent of a moderately large decimal number, say 1947563. After making 21 successive divisions to tally the remainders of the binary form: 1110110-11011110101011, you will see why binary numbers are not used in human figuring. There are too many digits (binary numbers have about three times as many digits, on the average, as the equivalent decimal numbers) and the numbers, having so little variety, are difficult to recognize and remember. The mechanics of adding and multiplying binary numbers are very easy, however, as we shall see presently, and the simplicity (among other qualities) recommends them for use in computers.

Octal Numbers

Binary-decimal conversion can be simplified by introducing an intermediate conversion from binary to *octal numbers,* that is, numbers based on the powers of 8. The octal equivalents of binary numbers, and vice versa, can be read off by inspection. The binary number is arranged in groups of three digits (called triads) starting with the rightmost digit. With each of the three positions in each triad is associated the power of two of that position, that is, 4-2-1 respectively. The octal equivalent has one digit (from 0 to 7) for each triad, and the value of the octal digit is the sum of the powers of two in the triad. For example, the binary number 101010011 is converted to octal thus (reading downward from binary triads to octal digits):

Power of 2	④ 2 ①	4 ② 1	4 ② ①
Binary triads	1 0 1	0 1 0	0 1 1
Octal digits	5	2	3

The reverse conversion from octal to binary can be

formed by reading upward from the octal digit to the powers of 2 and putting down 1's under each power needed to form the octal digit.

Conversion from octal to decimal, the other essential step, is performed by multiplying the decimal values of the powers of 8 by the respective octal digits and adding the decimal products. Thus 523_8 is converted by

$$
\begin{array}{rl}
5 \times 8^2 = & 320 \\
2 \times 8^1 = & 16 \\
3 \times 8^0 = & 3 \\
\hline
& 339_{10}
\end{array}
$$

The reverse conversion is performed by successive divisions by eight and by tallying the remainders. The proof that $339_{10} = 523_8$ is

$$
\begin{array}{rl}
8\,)\ 339 & \\
\hline
42 & \text{remainder } 3 \\
8\,)\ \ 42 & \\
\hline
5 & \text{remainder } 2 \\
8\,)\ \ \ 5 & \\
\hline
0 & \text{remainder } 5
\end{array}
$$

In contrast, the direct conversion of 339_{10} to binary takes more figuring:

$$
\begin{array}{rl}
2\,)\ 339 & \\
\hline
169 & \text{remainder } 1 \\
2\,)\ 169 & \\
\hline
84 & \text{remainder } 1 \\
2\,)\ \ 84 & \\
\hline
42 & \text{remainder } 0 \\
2\,)\ \ 42 & \\
\hline
21 & \text{remainder } 0
\end{array}
$$

$$2 \,)\ \underline{21}$$
$$10 \quad \text{remainder } 1$$
$$2 \,)\ \underline{10}$$
$$5 \quad \text{remainder } 0$$
$$2 \,)\ \underline{5}$$
$$2 \quad \text{remainder } 1$$
$$2 \,)\ \underline{2}$$
$$1 \quad \text{remainder } 0$$
$$2 \,)\ \underline{1}$$
$$0 \quad \text{remainder } 1$$

Arranged from bottom to top, the remainders are 101010011, which checks with the number previously given.

To show how useful octal conversion is, we return to the binary equivalent of 1947563_{10}. When this is arranged in triads 111 011 011 011 110 101 011, we readily read off the octal equivalent 7 3 3 3 6 5 3 by remembering the powers of two in each triad, 4-2-1, and adding the powers matched by the 1's in each triad.

Binary Addition and Subtraction

The next subject to review is the basic operation of binary arithmetic, addition. Let us first look at decimal addition, if only to realize how cumbersome it is. The common routine for summing a column of decimal numbers is to add them two at a time, starting with the topmost pair. Their sum is added to the digit immediately below, and so on to the bottom of the column. Whenever any sum in this process exceeds nine, we carry a 1 digit to the next column to the left. When we add the next column, we include all the carry digits that have been accumulated. It is

29

apparent that to add decimal digits we have to remember the 100 combinations of every digit 0
through 9 with every other. We commit these sums
to memory so early in life and make them so much a
part of ourselves that we forget the formal relationships and have to look twice to recognize the decimal
addition table:

+	0	1	2	3	4	5	6	7	8	9
0	0	1	2	3	4	5	6	7	8	9
1	1	2	3	4	5	6	7	8	9	10
2	2	3	4	5	6	7	8	9	10	11
3	3	4	5	6	7	8	9	10	11	12
4	4	5	6	7	8	9	10	11	12	13
5	5	6	7	8	9	10	11	12	13	14
6	6	7	8	9	10	11	12	13	14	15
7	7	8	9	10	11	12	13	14	15	16
8	8	9	10	11	12	13	14	15	16	17
9	9	10	11	12	13	14	15	16	17	18

The binary addition table comes from the upper
lefthand corner of the decimal table:

+	0	1
0	0	1
1	1	*

The asterisk takes the place of the 2, since there is
no digit 2 in binary. The binary equivalent of 2 is
10, or "0 and carry 1." So the binary table is

+	0	1
0	0	1
1	1	0 and carry 1

The rule for adding a column of binary digits follows that for decimal digits. Every time a sum ex-

ceeds 1, we carry a digit to the next column to the left.

In the following examples of binary addition we have placed the carry digits at the top of the column, and where a second carry digit is necessary, we have placed it on top of the first.

Example 1: Add 110010111 and 1010011

```
      1 111      Carry digits
  110010111      Augend
+   1010011      Addend
  ─────────
  111101010      Sum
```

Example 2: Add 101, 111, 001, 110

```
    1   ⎫
  1111  ⎬ Carry digits
   101  ⎭ Augend
   111    Addend
   001    Addend
   110    Addend
  ─────
 10011    Sum
```

As a check on Example 2, we can form from inspection the decimal equivalents of the four binary numbers: $5 + 7 + 1 + 6 = 19$. Also, $10011_2 = 16 + 0 + 0 + 2 + 1 = 19_{10}$ (Q.E.D.).

Binary subtraction, the reverse of addition, may be performed (as in decimals) by borrowing from the next column to the left whenever a difference falls below 0. The result is checked by adding the difference to the subtrahend to produce the minuend.

31

Example 3: Subtract 1001100 from 10101101 and check by addition

10101101	Minuend
1001100	Subtrahend
1	Borrow digit
01100001	Difference

Check:

1	Carry digit
1001100	Subtrahend
1100001	Difference
10101101	Minuend (Q.E.D.)

Example 4: Subtract 1101, 1001, 1111 and 0010 from 1100110. Check by addition.

1100110	Minuend
1101	Subtrahend
1001	Subtrahend
1111	Subtrahend
0010	Subtrahend
111111	Borrow digits
11111	Borrow digits
1	Borrow digit
111111	Difference

Check:

1101	
1001	
1111	
0010	
100111	Sum of subtrahends
+ 111111	Difference
1100110	Minuend (Q.E.D.)

32

Binary Multiplication and Division

Multiplication is repeated addition, the multiplicand being added, first to zero and then to the successive sums, as many times as the number of the multiplier. We avoid this cumbersome process for everyday use and substitute the format of long multiplication, which requires us to produce on demand the product of any digit, 0 through 9, by any other. Obviously, we must have memorized the decimal multiplication table, shown here in formal array:

×	0	1	2	3	4	5	6	7	8	9
0	0	0	0	0	0	0	0	0	0	0
1	0	1	2	3	4	5	6	7	8	9
2	0	2	4	6	8	10	12	14	16	18
3	0	3	6	9	12	15	18	21	24	27
4	0	4	8	12	16	20	24	28	32	36
5	0	5	10	15	20	25	30	35	40	45
6	0	6	12	18	24	30	36	42	48	54
7	0	7	14	21	28	35	42	49	56	63
8	0	8	16	24	32	40	48	56	64	72
9	0	9	18	27	36	45	54	63	72	81

The binary multiplication table comes from the upper left-hand corner of the decimal table:

×	0	1
0	0	0
1	0	1

When we apply this simple table to long multiplication we find that every 1 in the multiplier repeats the multiplicand, and the zeroes contribute nothing at all. We must keep track of the places (that is, align the products under the proper digits), but otherwise long multiplication is simple.

Example 5: Multiply 101100101 by 1011

```
        101100101
×            1011
        101100101
        101100101
        000000000
        101100101
      111101010111
```

Long division in binary follows the decimal pattern.

Example 6: Check Example 5 by dividing the product by the multiplier to obtain the multiplicand.

```
              101100101   (Q.E.D.)
      1011)111101010111
           1011
           1000
           0000
           10001
           1011
           1100
           1011
             11
             00
            110
            000
            1101
            1011
             101
             000
             1011
             1011
             0000
```

Digits and Electric Currents

So much for human figuring in binary numbers. Computers can figure by the passage of electrical current. For example, we agree that an electrical circuit in which current flows will represent the digit 1; if no current flows, the circuit represents the digit 0. A circuit containing a lamp, a battery, and a switch (Fig. 6) illustrates the method. When the

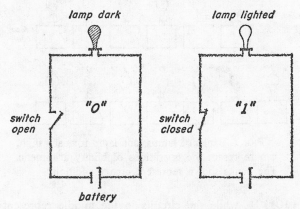

FIG. 6. Binary digits can be represented by current in an electric circuit. When the switch is open, no current can flow and the circuit is in the "0" condition; when closed, current flows and "1" condition is represented.

switch is closed, current flows and the lamp lights: the circuit is in the "1" condition. When the switch is open and no current can flow, the lamp is dark: the circuit is in the "0" condition.

By placing several such circuits side by side, and

35

by throwing the respective switches on or off, we can represent a binary number. The bank of six circuits at the top in Fig. 7 represents the number

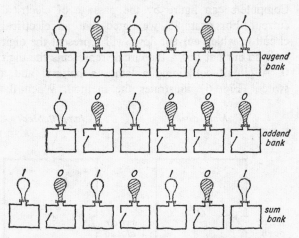

FIG. 7. Banks of lamps, one lamp for each digit, can represent the operations of binary arithmetic. The banks shown represent binary addition.

101101, while the circuits in the middle represent the number 101000. If we wish the circuits to add these numbers we must cause the current flowing (or not flowing) in one of the top lamps to be associated with the current in the lamp immediately below it. The combined currents are represented by the lamps at the bottom of the figure. Since the sum 1010101 has seven digits, we need seven lamps, the leftmost to represent the leftmost carry digit.

The rules for combining the currents are those given by the binary addition table:

Rule 1: $0 + 0 = 0$
Rule 2: $0 + 1 = 1$
Rule 3: $1 + 0 = 1$
Rule 4: $1 + 1 = 0$, and carry 1.

A circuit that obeys the first three rules is shown in Fig. 8. If switches A and B are both open, the sum

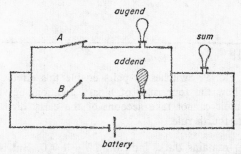

FIG. 8. This simple circuit follows three of the rules of binary addition, but gives a wrong result for the fourth rule.

lamp remains dark (condition "0") and represents the first rule. If either switch A or switch B is closed, the lamp lights (condition "1"), representing the second and third rules. But this circuit gives a wrong result for the fourth rule, since the lamp lights when both switches are closed, whereas it should remain dark. Moreover, in this last case we must have some way of indicating the carry digit of the fourth rule.

To represent all four rules we need a different circuit, one containing four switches operated in pairs, as in Fig. 9. As shown, this circuit represents $0 + 0 = 0$. If the augend switch is pushed down and the addend switch left as it is, the sum lamp lights, indicating $1 + 0 = 1$. With both switches down the

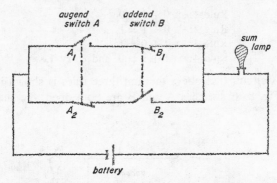

FIG. 9. Switches in pairs enable this circuit to follow the four rules of binary addition, but the circuit cannot take account of the carry digit of the fourth rule.

lamp remains dark, indicating $1 + 1 = 0$. But in the latter case we must indicate also that a carry digit has been formed.

To show the presence or absence of the carry digit we can add two additional switches and another lamp, shown at the top of Fig. 10. In this circuit, for example, when both switches are down, the carry lamp lights and the sum lamp remains dark, indicating $1 + 1 = 0$ with 1 to carry. The circuit of Fig. 10 is called a "half-adder" circuit. Later we shall see how these can be used in pairs in a computer to add binary numbers.

Subtraction can be expressed by a subtraction table:

		Minuend	
−		0	1
Subtrahend	0	0	1
	1	1 and borrow 1	0

38

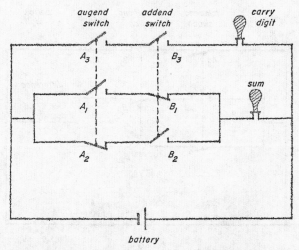

FIG. 10. "Half-adder" circuit uses two sets of three switches to add binary digits and to indicate the carry digit.

This array has the same form as the binary addition table, except for the location of the borrow digit. Hence, the same circuit (Fig. 11) serves for binary subtraction, except that switch A_3 is closed when the minuend switch is up, whereas in the addition circuit, A_3 is open when the augend switch is up. This circuit is a "half-subtractor."

Figure 12 shows how an augend 111 is added to an addend 110. The rightmost digits, 1 and 0 respectively, operate the zero-order adder, producing a sum digit 1 and a carry digit 0, which passes to the left and so on. When all augend digits, addend digits, and carry digits have been accounted for (as in the third-order adder shown), the addition is complete. Note that all the adders (except the zero-

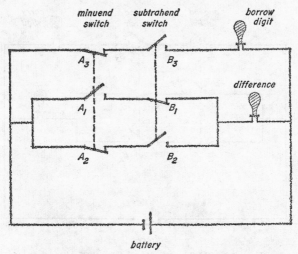

FIG. 11. "Half-subtractor" circuit subtracts binary digits and indicates the borrow digit. It is the same as the adder circuit, except that the open and closed conditions of switch A_3 are reversed.

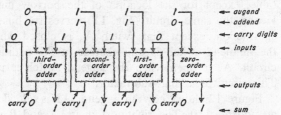

FIG. 12. Four adder circuits operating in parallel. Each passes the carry digit, if any, to its neighbor on the left. Shown are the digits of the sum $111 + 110 = 1101$.

order one) have three inputs (augend digit, addend digit, carry digit passed from the right) and two outputs (sum digit and carry digit to be passed to the left). We shall examine adder circuits in more detail in Chapter 6.

Multiplication and Division

In multiplication, as we have said, the multiplicand is added to zero as many times as the number of the multiplier. Such repeated additions can be used in computers, but the procedure of long multiplication (forming the product of the multiplicand by each digit of the multiplier, shifting the position of each product to agree with the position of the digit, and adding the products) is preferred because it is simpler and faster. In a typical scheme of computer multiplication the digits of the multiplier are read off from left to right. Each 1-digit reproduces the multiplicand; each 0-digit produces a zero for every digit in the multiplicand. These results are "lined up" with the digits that produced them. Each such result is added to the previous sum. When all the digits of the multiplier are "used up," the final sum is the product.

We can illustrate this by using the numbers of Example 5, page 34:

101100101	Multiplicand
×1011	Multiplier
101100101	First step (multiplicand reproduced by leftmost digit of multiplier)
000000000	Second step (0's from next digit)
1011001010	Sum
101100101	Third step (multiplicand reproduced by next digit)
11011111001	Sum
101100101	Fourth step (multiplicand reproduced by last digit)
111101010111	Sum (=product)

Note that the addend of each addition is shifted one place to the right of the previous addend. To shift a number replace a given digit by the adjacent digit. Electrically the current in one circuit is replaced by the current in the adjacent circuit. In binary circuits only two cases occur: if the adjacent digits are the same no change is required; if they are different the currents must be interchanged. The circuits that perform the shifting operation are known as *shift registers*.

Division in computers follows the routine of long division, except that the format may be somewhat different. In one typical routine the divisor is held in a fixed position and the dividend is shifted to the left, one place at a time. At each place the digits of the dividend are compared with those of the divisor. When the divisor digits are larger than the dividend digits, a 0 is written in the quotient and the dividend is shifted left. When the divisor digits are equal to or smaller than the dividend digits, a 1 is written in the quotient, the divisor is subtracted from the dividend, and the difference is written down as a new dividend. This dividend is then shifted to the left and the process repeats until all the dividend digits are used up.

As an example of this computer format for division, we repeat Example 6 (page 34). Note that the position of the divisor remains fixed, and the dividends are shifted to the left:

		Quotient Digits
111101010111	Dividend	
1011	Divisor (larger)	0
111101010111	Dividend shifted left	
1011	Divisor (larger)	0
111101010111	Dividend shifted left	
1011	Divisor (larger)	0
111101010111	Dividend shifted left	
1011	Divisor (smaller)	1
10001010111	Difference (new dividend)	
10001010111	Dividend shifted left	
1011	Divisor (larger)	0
10001010111	Dividend shifted left	
1011	Divisor (smaller)	1
110010111	Difference (new dividend)	
110010111	Dividend shifted left	
1011	Divisor (smaller)	1
110111	Difference (new dividend)	
110111	Dividend shifted left	
1011	Divisor (larger)	0
110111	Dividend shifted left	
1011	Divisor (larger)	0
110111	Dividend shifted left	
1011	Divisor (smaller)	1
1011	Difference (new dividend)	

1011	Dividend shifted left	
1011	Divisor (larger)	0
1011	Dividend shifted left	
1011	Divisor (equal)	1
0000	Difference (no remainder)	

The quotient digits, taken from the top to bottom, are 000101100101. Neglecting the first three 0's (which have no significance), we find this result agrees with the quotient of Example 6.

It has been worthwhile to write out this cumbersome routine for long division in full because it illustrates one of the basic facts of the world of computers: the rules must be simple, completely stated, and followed to the letter. The divisor is compared with dividend digits just above it. The quotient digit is 0 if the divisor is larger than the digits just above it. The quotient digit is 1 if the divisor is equal to or smaller than the digits just above it. The existing dividend is shifted one place to the left, after each quotient digit is found. A new dividend is formed after a quotient digit of 1 is formed. The new dividend is the difference between the divisor and the existing dividend. These statements express the logic of long division. The computer circuits used in division embody this logic.

Having now examined the routines of arithmetic used by computers (addition, subtraction, shifting right, shifting left, comparing two numbers to see whether one is equal to, smaller than, or larger than the other), we are now ready to use them in a full-scale computation—solving simultaneous equations in algebra.

44

CHAPTER 3

HOW COMPUTERS COMPUTE

What can be said at all, can be said clearly.
—LUDWIG WITTGENSTEIN

To illustrate how the basic operations of computer arithmetic are used in a full-scale electronic computation, we will take a familiar example from algebra, two simultaneous equations, and show how a computer can find the unknowns from the given quantities. We shall start with the methods used by a human calculator, and then show how the computer follows the same routine. As we go through the steps of the human computation we find that, besides doing the arithmetic proper, we must write down (*store*) the numbers produced (sums, differences, products, and quotients) and look them up (*retrieve* them) as they are needed in later steps. A computer must also store and retrieve numbers.

A human computer must *preside* over the computation, performing each step in proper order. An electronic computer must do the same, and it has a particular piece of equipment, the *control unit,* which looks up each instruction and sees to it that

45

the other parts of the computer perform each step in order.

Figure 13 proposes the analogy between human

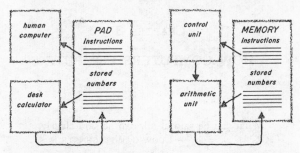

FIG. 13. Tools of computation, for people and computers.

and machine computation. With pencil and pad man writes down instructions for the computation and stores the numbers to be needed in the process. In the computation itself he operates the desk calculator. The arrows show the flow of information: read the instructions; operate the calculator to get the result called for in the instruction; store the result on the paper; read the next instruction; retrieve from paper stored number or numbers required by next instruction and transfer to desk calculator; proceed in same manner until all instructions have been satisfied.

A computer performs the same routine. The instructions are stored in the memory unit (the computer equivalent of the pad of paper). These are "read" by the control unit, which directs the arithmetic unit to perform the step specified in the instruction. The result is stored in the memory unit. When an instruction calls for a previously stored number, the control unit transfers the number from the memory to the arithmetic unit. Thus there are three main functions in computation: *storage and retrieval* of instructions and numbers, *processing* of numbers by arithmetic, and *control* of the operations by reference to the program of instructions.

The instructions must be on hand before the computation begins. When we solve a problem in algebra, we may not always be aware that we have prepared a program, but we have. We have our memorized knowledge of the steps of algebra and arithmetic, and we have in our mind's eye at least a rudimentary plan for the solution. The process can be illustrated aptly with the working out in detail of the following quite simple problem in algebra.

Two Simultaneous Equations

Given: the simultaneous equations

$$ax + by = c$$
$$dx + ey = f$$

Find: the unknowns x and y for given values of a, b, c, d, e, and f.

The first step in drawing up the program is to recast these equations so that x and y are given directly; that is, to find the solutions to the equations in general form. To "get rid of" y, we multiply the top equation by e, the bottom equation by b, subtract the results, and solve for x:

$$aex + bey = ce$$
$$\underline{bdx + bey = bf}$$
$$x(ae - bd) \qquad = ce - bf$$
$$x = \frac{ce - bf}{ae - bd}$$

47

A similar manipulation produces *y:*

$$y = \frac{af - cd}{ae - bd}$$

Inspection of these equations for x and y shows that we need first to form six products: *ae, af, bd, bf, cd,* and *ce.* Then we need to form three differences of these products: $ce - bf, af - cd,$ and $ae - bd.$ Finally we need two quotients of these differences $(ce - bf) / (ae - bd)$ and $(af - cd) / (ae - bd)$ which give the results x and $y,$ respectively.

We have reduced the solution of two simultaneous algebraic equations to eleven steps in arithmetic: six multiplications, three subtractions, and two divisions. We must perform them in order; the divisions must await the results of the subtractions, and the subtractions cannot be performed until we have the products. To have all these results on hand when needed, we store them by writing them down on the pad.

Writing the Program

Now we are ready to write the program:
1. Write down the given values *a, b, c, d, e,* and *f.*
2. Compute the product *ae* and write it down.
3. Repeat step 2 for product *af.*
4. Repeat step 2 for product *bd.*
5. Repeat step 2 for product *bf.*
6. Repeat step 2 for product *cd.*
7. Repeat step 2 for product *ce.*
8. Subtract the result of step 5 from the result of step 7, and write down the result, $ce - bf.$

9. Repeat step 8, using the results of steps 6 and 3 respectively, to obtain $af - cd$.

10. Repeat step 8, using the results of steps 4 and 2 respectively, to obtain $ae - bd$.

11. Divide the result of step 8 by the result of step 10. Write down the result. This is the value of the unknown x.

12. Divide the result of step 9 by the result of step 10. Write down the result. This is the value of the unknown y.

For particular values of a through f ($30x - 16y = 12$; $10x + 6y = 38$), the twelve steps committed to the writing pad compose this table:

Step	Stored Data
1.	$a = 30$; $b = -16$; $c = 12$; $d = 10$; $e = 6$; $f = 38$
2.	$ae = 180$
3.	$af = 1140$
4.	$bd = -160$
5.	$bf = -608$
6.	$cd = 120$
7.	$ce = 72$
8.	$ce - bf = 680$
9.	$af - cd = 1020$
10.	$ae - bd = 340$
11.	$(ce - bf)/(ae - bd) = 2$ (Answer $x = 2$)
12.	$(af - cd)/(ae - bd) = 3$ (Answer $y = 3$)

In forming the products, differences, and quotients we must *locate* the appropriate numbers on the pad. Thus to form product ae, we locate 30 alongside a, and 6 alongside e. These acts of location are performed without conscious effort. Our eyes, glancing over the pad, recognize the letters and the associated numbers, but the casual facility is the fruit of much practice in arithmetic and algebra.

A computer must have very explicit instructions to perform acts of location. It must be told to put a result in a particular place; to retrieve the result it must be told to go back to that particular place. Each place in its memory has an "address" or "memory location," which must be stated whenever a number is to be placed in, or retrieved from, that place. Memory locations usually are given as numbers, like street numbers.

The program cited contains five specific instructions: multiply, subtract, divide, write down, and repeat. There is, in addition, a sixth instruction that is not stated explicitly but is followed: look up the result (of step so-and-so). A human computer acts on these six instructions without conscious attention, but an electronic computer must have explicit statements.

Before the data, addresses, and commands fed into the computer can be recognized and acted upon within the control unit, they must be translated into binary numbers. There are, therefore, three different kinds of binary numbers that a computer uses: for data (given values, intermediate results, answers), for memory locations, and for commands. The computer must distinguish among these numbers; utter confusion will result if a computer by mistake substitutes a memory-location number for a command number or a data number. To show how a computer keeps things straight, we shall run through the problem of simultaneous equations as it would be performed by a computer.

Computer Instructions

Groups of numbers and letters known as "computer words" are presented to the computer as instructions. These words contain symbols for the operation to be performed and one or more sets of numbers to specify memory locations where the information to be operated upon will be found or is to be stored.

Depending on the design of the machines, computer words take different forms. In this chapter* we shall use words of four parts. The first part specifies the operation to be performed; the second and third give the memory locations where the numbers to be operated upon are to be found; and the fourth gives the memory location where the result is to be placed. Each part consists of three letters or numbers. Our computer word then looks like this:

Operation Code First Memory Address
(3 characters)   (3 numbers)
Second Memory Address Third Memory Address
      (3 numbers)   (3 numbers)

We use the following code letters for operations:

Operation Code	*Meaning*
LOD ("load")	Load a number into the computer, and place it at the memory address specified in the first memory address.
MUL ("multiply")	Multiply the numbers found at the first and second memory addresses and place the product at the third memory address.

---

* In Chapter 7 we will use words having only one memory address, since this is the form for which most modern computers are designed. The three-address words used here (now obsolescent) make the explanations simpler and shorter.

SUB ("subtract")	Subtract the number at the second memory address from the number at the first memory address and place the difference at the third memory address.
DIV ("divide")	Divide the number at the first memory address by the number at the second memory address and place the quotient at the third memory address.
PRT ("print")	Print out the number stored at the first memory address.

The memory addresses, having three numerals each, can be identified by any of the numbers 000 through 999. Thus, our computer has available 1000 different memory addresses. Our program will use them in numerical order.

Now let us write a computer instruction for each of the twelve steps in the program for two simultaneous equations. We start with the six given quantities *a* through *f* punched out on punched cards, which the computer "reads" when instructed to load the values of *a* through *f* into the computer. The steps are numbered to correspond with the "human" program, and the computer program then becomes:

Step	*Computer Word*	*Explanation*
1a.	LOD 000	Read the first punched card (containing the number *a*) and place the number at memory location 000.

52

1b.	LOD 001	Read b, place it at location 001.
1c.	LOD 002	Read c, place it at location 002.
1d.	LOD 003	Read d, place it at location 003.
1e.	LOD 004	Read e, place it at location 004.
1f.	LOD 005	Read f, place it at location 005.
2.	MUL 000 004 006	Multiply a by e, place product at location 006.
3.	MUL 000 005 007	Multiply a by f, place product at location 007.
4.	MUL 001 003 008	Multiply b by d, place product at location 008.
5.	MUL 001 005 009	Multiply b by f, place product at location 009.
6.	MUL 002 003 010	Multiply c by d, place product at location 010.
7.	MUL 002 004 011	Multiply c by e, place product at location 011.
8.	SUB 011 009 012	Subtract bf from ce, place difference at location 012.
9.	SUB 007 010 013	Subtract cd from af, place difference at location 013.
10.	SUB 006 008 014	Subtract bd from ae, place difference at location 014.
11.	DIV 012 014 015	Divide $ce - bf$ by $ae - bd$, place quotient at location 015.
12.	DIV 013 014 016	Divide $af - cd$ by $ae - bd$, place quotient at location 016.

This completes the computation, and we have the answers stored at memory locations 015 and 016. To retrieve these, we add two instructions:

13.   PRT 015   Print out the number at 015 (value of x).

14.   PRT 016   Print out the number at 016 (value of y).

Finally we issue the order to stop:

15.   STP.

The computer is ready now to be cleared of all the numbers stored in locations 000 through 016, so that it may be used on the next problem.

Storing the Program

This example suggests how a computer carries out the twenty instructions of this program (there are six steps in Step 1) and prints out the answers. Not yet explained is how the computer receives the instructions embodied in the computer words. One way would be for the operator to type each instruction on the computer's input typewriter, waiting for each instruction to be acted upon before typing in the next. But this procedure would be very slow and, if many pairs of simultaneous equations were to be solved, very tedious. So, except in a training course, this routine is never followed. The operator uses the typewriter only to ask for a specific item of information, or to correct a specific mistake. In the normal performance of a program the computer is arranged to do all the work. In fact, a computer can find the solutions to thousands of pairs of simultaneous equations, printing out the answers as they are found, *entirely without human intervention.*

The computer can control itself if, before the computation starts, it is programmed to store the first nineteen instructions (omitting the instruction to stop) in the computer memory at locations 101 through 119. Two additional instructions are added to the program. These are:

16.	CLR 000 016	Clear the memory of all numbers in locations 000 through 016, inclusive.
17.	RPT 101	Repeat the computation starting with the instructions at location 101.

These instructions are stored at locations 120 and 121.

Now let us see what happens when the start button is pressed. The computer reads the first instruction, at location 101, which tells it to read the values of the first set of given quantities (*a* through *f*) from punched cards. It then proceeds through the program by consulting each stored instruction, in locations 102 through 119, one after another. This routine causes the computer to print out the answers for the first pair of equations. Then, by the instruction located at 120, it clears the numbers for that solution and, by the instruction at location 121, returns to the instruction at location 101. The next set of given quantities (*a* through *f*) is read in, solved, printed, the numbers cleared, and the process repeated over and over until the last pair of equations is solved.

The computer must be instructed to stop. Otherwise it would attempt new solutions even after the stack of punched cards had run out. A count must be kept (in a *counter circuit*) of the number of times the RPT ("repeat") command is issued. Suppose there are 500 pairs of equations to be solved. The computation must be stopped when the counter reaches 500. At that time the final instruction is issued: STP ("stop"). How does the counter "know" it has reached 500? By subtracting its count from the number 500 stored in another location. So long as the difference is positive, 500 has not been reached, and the RPT command is issued. But when the difference is zero 500 has been reached, the RPT command is not issued, and the STP command appears in its place.

As this process proceeds, 500 pairs of answers are printed out, one pair for each repetition of the program. For identification of the answers the computer can be arranged to print out the corresponding reading of the counter, and also the values of the quantities *a* through *f* associated with each pair of answers.

This is an oversimplified and somewhat naïvely expressed version of the process (as those familiar with actual computer operations will testify). It has been drawn up to illustrate the main ideas while sparing you incidental details that would obscure basic principles. In summary, computers compute in this wise: The problem is cast, by the human programmer, into a series of instructions which state, step by step, what the computer does, where it gets its information, and where it stores the result. The program is then loaded into the computer; that is, the computer words for each instruction are placed at specified memory locations. The input data (example, values of a through f) are stored, typically on punched cards which are read as the need arises, or they may be loaded into the computer at other specified memory locations.

The control unit then consults the memory location of the first instruction, examines the instruction, and directs the computer to follow it, and store the result at the specified location. The control unit consults the memory again, at the location where the second instruction is stored, follows this instruction, and stores the result. Each instruction is acted upon in turn until answers are found and (usually) printed out. If the computation is to be repeated for new input data, the control unit, encountering the instruction to repeat, examines the location where the first instruction remains stored, and repeats the program, step by step. When all the repetitions are completed, the program counter transfers the next instruction from "repeat" to "stop."

Encoding Computer Instructions

One piece of unfinished business remains. In the previous chapter we dealt with binary arithmetic and stated that computers work, in the last analysis, only with the two digits 0 and 1. Yet, in this chapter we have presented computer instructions in letters and the decimal digits. Also, we have placed these letters and digits in memory locations designated by decimal digits. Obviously, such letters and decimal digits must be translated into binary digits before the computer can work with them. This translation is known as *binary encoding*, since it substitutes for each letter and decimal digit a *code character* made up of only 0's and 1's. This translation is performed automatically by the input equipment feeding the computer. For example, the input typewriter contains several electric circuits (typically a group of six or eight circuits), which are actuated by each typewriter key. In the IBM Model 1401 each typewriter key operates eight circuits. Six represent the code for the letters and numbers, one represents a "word mark" signifying the beginning of a computer word, and the remaining circuit checks the accuracy of the encoding process.

Suppose we are to type on the Model 1401 typewriter the symbol for ADD, where the first "A" is the beginning of a computer word. When we press the "A" key, the typewriter circuits open and close to form the following code word: 10110001. Each time we press the "D" key, the code word 01110100 is passed on to the computer. When we press the numeral keys, the rightmost digits in the eight-digit code are the respective binary equivalents. Thus in 1401 language the code for the decimal digit 9 is 00001001, since $9_{10} = 1001_2$.

Different sets of code characters and words are used in different computers. Most computers communicate with the outside world through the letters and decimal digits, since these are most readily comprehended by the operator. The translation processes are built into the computer equipment, and the operator need not concern himself with 0's and 1's.

Information is stored in the computer memory also in the form of 0's and 1's. Each memory location must possess a sufficient number of individual memory "cells" to accommodate all the 0's and 1's of the code words to be stored there. Since memory cells in large numbers are expensive, and since putting words into memory and looking them up takes valuable time, the structure of the computer memory and the structure of the computer language must be planned carefully to avoid waste of time and money. We will examine the organization of a typical computer memory in more detail in Chapter 6.

This chapter has examined only the rudiments of electronic computation. Computing solutions to simultaneous equations, however useful as an introductory example, is a far cry from beating a champion at his own game. To appreciate how computers can be used in intellectual tasks calls for deeper understanding of computer language and the logical processes which transform thought into computer instructions.

CHAPTER 4

TWO KINDS OF LANGUAGE

> Perhaps of all the creations of man, language is the
> most astonishing.—LYTTON STRACHEY

Language is the brain's major tool. Conscious
thought uses words and phrases, and it seems certain
that word-like patterns are employed in the unconscious processes of the mind. It is not surprising,
then, that the major tool of computer intelligence
also should be a language. There must be links, of
course, between the language of people and the language of the machine. Although syntactical analysis
is outside the domain of this book, it will be necessary in this chapter to examine some structural relationships of the two languages.

The Symbols of Natural Language

The keyboard of the typewriter I use in writing
this book illustrates the symbols of natural language.
It contains eighty-three different characters (letters,
digits, fractions, punctuation marks, and abbreviations), and it provides the most used symbol of all,

the *space* between words, made by the space bar. For the moment, we restrict our attention to the twenty-six capital letters of the English alphabet and the all-important space. With these twenty-seven symbols we can spell out the numerals and punctuation marks and all the other symbols.

With time and patience, by striking only these twenty-six letters and the space bar *in the proper order,* you or I can re-create anything written in the English language. Note the emphasis on "in the proper order." Everything in language depends on order. Even a minor mix-up in the proper ordering of letters and spaces can reduce the finest phrase to gibberish, and certain errors in striking the keys will alter or reverse the meaning without leaving a clue.

To achieve this proper order in language, we must agree first on an alphabet and adopt conventions on the ordering of the letters (proper spelling) to form words. Secondly, we must assign proper meanings to words, individually and in context. Thirdly, we must accept rules of grammar establishing the order of words in phrases and sentences. Fourthly, we must develop and obey laws of logic in the association of the ideas expressed by words, phrases, sentences, and paragraphs. If we violate these rules, we disrupt —even destroy—the communication of thought.

Sentences in the English language can be classified according to both their character (declarative, imperative, interrogative, exclamatory) and their form (simple, compound, complex). All these types and forms appear also in computer language. Indeed, the exclamation, "Stop! A necessary instruction has been omitted," occurs sometimes with disheartening frequency when a program of computation is being debugged.

Another Computer Program for Humans

To make the comparison between natural and artificial languages more concrete, let us return to the series for calculating π (Chapter 1) and use natural language in writing instructions for carrying out a test computation.

In our "π calculation" there are four different groups of sentences needed to instruct, command, and guide the person who performs the computation. The first are declarative sentences that state the subject matter of the computation and all the necessary data, known in advance, which bear on the solution. The second is an imperative sentence commanding the desired result. The third is a group of imperative sentences directing the computation. With these sentences at hand, the human computer is ready to go to work. Then a fourth group of imperative sentences, formed and executed within his mind, comes into play. These direct his hands and eyes to operate the desk calculator and to record or look up the intermediate steps and final results. Since these statements, instructions, and directions are very similar to those that would be used in programming an electronic computer, they are worthy of detailed attention here.

First, the following declarative statements define the subject matter and state the facts:

D-1. There is a series for π consisting of the sum of certain fractions.

D-2. The series has no end.

D-3. All the fractions in the series have the numerator 4.

D-4. The denominators of the fractions are, successively, the odd integers, beginning with 1.

D-5. The successive fractions have opposite signs, beginning with plus.

D-6. The sum of the series may be terminated at any point to obtain an approximate value of π.

D-7. If the last term prior to the termination has a plus sign, the approximation is too large.

D-8. If the last term prior to the termination has a minus sign, the approximation is too small.

D-9. Averaging of too-small and too-large values will result in a more accurate intermediate value.

D-10. The following tools are available: a desk calculator, a pad of paper, and a pencil.

D-11. The value of π, to eight decimal places, is 3.14159265+.

Note that *all* the required information is given, whether or not the person tackling the problem may be expected to know some of the facts. It is even desirable to make certain statements (such as D-7 and D-8) which may be deduced from one of the other statements (D-5), since we are not sure of the hypothetical human computer's reasoning power. At this stage, we assume only his ability to read and understand each of the eleven declarative sentences.

Next comes the imperative sentence that commands the desired result:

I-0. Determine whether the value of π, correct to six decimal places, can be obtained by computing 100 terms of the series and averaging their sums.

Then come the imperative sentences directing the steps of the computation:

I-1. *Compute* the first 100 terms of the series and *record* the value and sign of each term on the paper.

I-2. *Add* the first 98 terms and *record* the sum on the pad as the "98-term sum."

I-3. *Add* the 99th term to the 98-term sum and *record* the sum on the pad as the "99-term sum."

I-4. *Add* the 100th term to the 99-term sum and *record* the sum on the pad as the "100-term sum."

I-5. *Compare* the 98-term sum with the given value of π. *If* the sum is smaller *proceed* to the next step; *if not* there is an error. In the latter event *check* all work in steps I-1 and I-2 to correct the error, then *proceed*.

I-6. *Compare* the 99-term sum with the given value of π. *If* the sum is larger *proceed* to the next step; *if not* there is an error. *Check* previous work to correct the error, then *proceed*.

I-7. *Compare* the 100-term sum with the given value of π. *If* the sum is smaller *proceed* to the next step; *if not* there is an error. *Check* previous work to locate error, then *proceed*.

I-8. *Add* the 98-term sum to the 99-term sum and *divide* the result by two. *Record* this as the "98–99 average."

I-9. *Add* the 99-term sum to the 100-term sum and *divide* the result by two. *Record* this as the "99–100 average."

I-10. *Add* the 98–99 average to the 99–100 average and *divide* the result by two. *Record* the result as the "98–99–99–100 average."

I-11. *Compare* the 98–99–99–100 average with the given value of π. *If* the numbers agree exactly, up to and including the sixth decimal place,

64

write "problem solved," on pad and hand to instructor. *If not, write* "problem unsolved" on pad and hand to instructor.

I-12. *Clear* the calculator of all numbers, tear off work sheets, sharpen pencil for next problem.

I-13. *Stop* and await further instructions.

If you have had the patience to follow these steps, you will find (italicized) the following key imperative words: compute, record, add, divide, proceed, check, write, clear, and stop. These are key words of computer language. We also meet the word "compare" in Steps I-5, I-6, I-7, and I-11, followed by one alternative, "if so," or by the other, "if not." These comparisons also are typical processes in computer language, called "branch points," where the computation proceeds one way or another, depending upon the result of the command.

In this exercise, we have gone a way toward closing the gap between natural language and computer language. But this is an easy case of instructions to carry out a computation. We can close the gap in a much more significant way if we consciously examine our thinking processes and see how often we find ourselves defining an idea by a declarative statement, combining such statements with connectives, issuing commands to ourselves to repeat, to add, to subtract, to compare, to go one way "if" such-and-such an idea is "true," the other way "if not true." In the subtle variety of our thoughts, we can catch many a glimpse of logical processes of language that shape our understanding, our reasoning, and our actions. The opportunity for such self-inspection being personal, though universal, we leave it as "an exercise for the student."

Characters as Abbreviations

A probably indispensable device in language is the single character used as an abbreviation. The numerals and punctuation marks on the typewriter keyboard are examples, as are all the letters. The initials of your name identify you to a sufficiently close approximation; mine identify me. In fact (thanks to the existence of such proper names as Quentin, Xavier, and Zola) most of the 17,576 three-letter combinations of the English alphabet are used to identify people. Similarly, in computer language single characters appear often as abbreviations for the most commonly used words.

These abbreviations, like the words they represent, almost always have several different meanings in natural language, and their recognition depends on the context. Since such multiple meanings would greatly complicate machine operation, the common abbreviations are defined in computer language to have but one meaning; whenever another meaning must be used it is defined in the particular context of the specific problem.

In natural language the commonest abbreviation is the period. This mark means "end of sentence," or "this is an abbreviation," or "decimal point." In Model 1401 computer language* it means "Stop" when used to instruct the computer, and "radix

---

* Throughout this chapter, to be definite and consistent, we will use the symbols, definitions, and operations of the electronic computer most widely used at the time of writing, the IBM Model 1401. This is a variable-word-length binary-coded-decimal machine. The general principles outlined apply to all digital electronic computers.

66

point" when used with a number (to separate the integral part from the fractional part). Other punctuation marks and signs are similarly defined in computer language in specific ways. They include , ? ! % $ & = * ( ) - + # — just about every special symbol on the keyboard. As identified by the computer the meanings of these symbols have little to do with their everyday meanings, but since the computer meanings are defined and stored no harm comes of this.

Among the most useful abbreviations, in any language, are the numerals. Numbers have general meanings embodied in the acts of counting and placing things in order. The numeral "2" thus denotes *in general* either the cardinal concept of "twoness," that quality possessed in common by pairs of things, or the ordinal concept of "second" in a sequence of things. The most *specific* meaning denotes a particular digit in a number, the value of the digit depending on its position in the number. Thus the "2" in "12" denotes two units; in 120, two tens; and in 1222, two hundreds, two tens, and two units.

In computer language all these meanings of numbers must be employed, and the design of the computer and its program of computation must distinguish clearly between the meanings. Otherwise, the computer cannot use the number surely in the intended way.

The Digits of Computer Language

We now turn to the specific structure of computer language. Actually, there is a family of such languages, starting with "plain English" (or some abbreviated version of it), and proceeding from one language to another until the plain English has been translated into forms that the machine can "understand" and manipulate. The structure of natural language is built on characters and spaces, the architecture progressing to words and, as it becomes more complex, to sentences and paragraphs. In computer language, as previous chapters have pointed out, there is an additional element to start with. Its building blocks are the digits 0 and 1.

These binary digits, which lie at the very heart of computer technology, are called "bits" for short. Every character, word, and sentence in the computer program must be reduced ultimately to a string of bits (zeroes and ones) before the computer can recognize them, manipulate them, and produce an answer.

This necessity surely separates man from machine. Few men can read the zero and one combinations of the bit code. But the machine can do it with astonishing ease, speed, and accuracy. Take my initials (DGF). Translated into the Model 1401 eight-bit machine code, these letters become 10110-1000111011100110110! With practice I might memorize these twenty-four digits, but to recognize them on first sight is another matter! This horrible example is beggared by an actual computer instruction, which may contain (in a single line of the Model 1401 code) as many as eighty characters, each represented by a combination of eight zeroes and ones.

Is all this necessary? Why should the machine

code be so far separated from human recognition? Why should the machine recognize directly only two symbols? Why not the ten decimal digits? Or better, the twenty-six letters? Or better still, the eighty-three characters and the space of the standard typewriter keyboard?

The answer starts with the fact that digital electronic computers operate so rapidly that the recognition and manipulation of long strings of zeroes and ones occur hundreds or thousands of times as fast as a human being can recognize and manipulate the familiar forms of natural language. Given this time advantage, we can afford to design the machine so that its every part has to make the simplest possible logical choice, the choice between two alternatives. The positions on its punch cards need only be punched (1) or not punched (0). Its diodes and transistors need only be conducting (1) or not conducting (0). Its indicator lamps need only be on (1) or off (0). Its magnetic memory cores need only be magnetized clockwise (1) or counterclockwise (0). Its typewriter hammers need only strike (1) or not strike (0).

Most significant of all, perhaps, the computer logic in a language of zeroes and ones may be based on statements that are true (1) or false (0). In real life statements are seldom wholly true or wholly false. But when we attempt to use the principles of logic to reach conclusions we find the "partly true" statement so difficult to deal with that we recast the argument in terms of truth or falsity. Machines can hardly do better.

Thus far attempts to build an electronic computer dealing with more than two conditions of operation

(several attempts have been made) have proved
impractical, because such a computer would have
to distinguish the fundamentally different and in-
definite condition "partly on." The word "partly"
implies that the degree of "on-ness" must be measured against a standard. In a simple, slow-acting
machine using mechanical parts, like a desk adding
machine, ten conditions of rotation of the number
wheels can be distinguished. But in a complicated,
high-speed, electronic machine, the best answer thus
far found—from the standpoints of reliability and
cost—is the simplest: two conditions only. Nature
in designing the machine code of our nervous system
came (independently!) to the same conclusion, as
we shall see in Chapter 9.

Digits to Characters

So, the basic "bit" alphabet of the machine code
has only two symbols, 0 and 1. From our study of
natural language, we know how to use an alphabet
to form groups of symbols. Taken two at a time,
two symbols can be arranged in four ($= 2 \times 2$) different combinations (00, 01, 10, 11). Taken four at
a time, we have 16 ($= 2^4$) combinations; 5 symbols,
32 combinations; 6 symbols, 64 combinations; 7
symbols, 128 combinations, and so on. For every
extra symbol we add to the group, we double the
number of possible combinations. Now we are ready
to form the characters of machine language. We
simply write out a code list, matching each character
of natural language against an arrangement of zeroes and ones which we agree by convention will
always stand for that character.

So long as we use a different set of zeroes and ones for each different character, we are free to choose the sets of zeroes and ones to suit our fancy. But we are well advised to use certain guide lines in making the assignments, which will make the strings of digits easy for the machine to recognize and manipulate. A larger format of digits than necessary would be wasteful both of machinery and computation time. In assigning the codes for the numerals, it simplifies things greatly to choose code symbols that are in fact binary numbers (or numbers simply derived from them) which can be added, subtracted, multiplied, and divided by the logical steps of binary arithmetic. Finally, each code group must have a definite number of zeroes and ones, since this restriction will indicate where each character begins and ends, and will obviate the need for an extra symbol.

With these guide lines in mind, we may set up a code list as follows: First, we select the list of characters we wish to work with: the twenty-six capital letters A through Z (small letters are not of sufficient additional utility to be used in most applications), the ten decimal digits 0 through 9, and up to twenty-eight punctuation marks, indicators, and abbreviation signs. These sixty-four characters can be represented by sixty-four groups of six zeroes and ones each ($2^6 = 64$ provides enough combinations). We agree, therefore, to use six digits in every code group to represent the natural language characters.

First we assign, as the code group for each decimal digit, its value in binary arithmetic:

Natural Language Character	Machine Code Group
0	000000
1	000001
2	000010
3	000011
4	000100
5	000101
6	000110
7	000111
8	001000
9	001001

We recognize the binary values among the digits to the right in each group. The digits to the left in each group (which are used in the codes for the letters and punctuation marks) are filled with zeroes in the numeral code.

Next we assign code groups to the letters. The natural alphabet is broken up into three parts: A through I, J through R, and S through Z. For A through I, ones occupy the first and second positions in the group, followed in the remaining four positions by the binary designations of 1 through 9, one for each of the nine letters A through I. For J through R, one occupies only the first position, zero the second, and the same nine binary numbers follow thereafter. For S through Z, a zero has the first position and a one the second, followed by the binary numbers for 2 through 9. The code list for the letters thus becomes:

Natural Language Character	Machine Code Group
A	110001
B	110010
C	110011

D	110100
E	110101
F	110110
G	110111
H	111000
I	111001
J	100001
K	100010
L	100011
M	100100
N	100101
O	100110
P	100111
Q	101000
R	101001
S	010010
T	010011
U	010100
V	010101
W	010110
X	010111
Y	011000
Z	011001

The code groups for the punctuation marks and abbreviation signs have the binary numbers 1011 through 1111 (equivalent to the decimal numbers 11 through 15) in the rightmost four positions, in conjunction with ones or zeroes in the first and second positions.

Having defined each number, letter, and sign by a code group of six zeroes and ones, we next place two additional digits in front of each group, making eight digits in all. The first of these is a one whenever the character in question is the first character of a word (or in single-letter words, the only character).

It serves the purpose of the space in natural language. If this first digit is a zero the machine recognizes that the character in question is *not* the first (or only) character in a word.

The second of the two additional digits is called a "parity bit"; its purpose is to assist in detection of errors in the code groups. This second digit is chosen so that the total number of ones in the whole code group is always an even number. The machine is designed to reject any code group having an odd number of ones and to signal that an error has been detected.

To summarize: in Model 1401 computer language each character is represented by eight bits. The first if a 1 marks the beginning of a word. The second brings the total number of 1's in the group to an even number. The third and fourth distinguish between the three parts of the natural alphabet. The last four represent, first, the binary forms of the decimal digits and, secondly, the position of each letter in each part of the alphabet. The last six, in combinations not used for the numerals and letters, also represent the punctuation marks and special signs.

From Characters to Words

The next step is obvious. We make words by assembling one or more characters, taking care to place a one in the first place of the eight-digit code group whenever the character starts (or is) a computer word. At this level of computer language only very simple words are used. They are mainly one-character abbreviations chosen to facilitate human recognition of their meaning (they are called "mnemonics"—aids to the memory). Examples (in Model 1401 language) are the initials A, S, B, C, R, P, and W for such commands as *A*dd, *S*ubtract, *B*ranch, *C*ompare, *R*ead, *P*unch, and *W*rite. Others are two-character or three-character mnemonics, like CS, for *C*lear the *S*torage, or MCS for *M*ove *C*haracters and *S*uppress zeroes. These are instructive words, mainly verbs as they would be used in imperative sentences.

We must leave (for the next chapter) other types of computer words, particularly the connectives— *and, or, because, therefore,* and *if*—which figure so prominently in the logic of language. For the present we need only to summarize the properties of words in this relatively new language. A word in computer language (like a word in natural language) is a selected character or collection of characters *defined* in the character code list. It is not always pronounceable except phonetically (MCS is pronounced "emcee-ess"), but it is memorizable. Its meaning is precisely defined. It is from that store of words that not only is maintained in the minds of the computer specialists and in the dictionaries of computer language but also is storable in the memory of the computer. When so stored, it can be recognized and manipulated by the computer in the same way that people recognize and manipulate words in making sentences, solving problems, arriving at conclusions and, in short, thinking.

Translating Computer Language

We conclude this chapter with a brief glimpse of one of the most important procedures in computer language, translation from one level of computer language to another. The lowest order of computer language is the machine bit code, all but incomprehensible to the common man. It becomes intelligible only when translated to the next higher level, the mnemonic word language. How is this translation accomplished? Well, if we had the time and patience, we could translate Model 1401 computer digits by counting off the zeroes and ones in groups of eight, looking up the corresponding characters in the code list, and writing the characters out on paper. No intelligibility would emerge until we noted the characters that start words (each character having a one at the beginning of its code group). Then, with only a little practice, we could read the mnemonic words and, from their sequence, divine their meaning. We could translate the data words by looking up their meanings in the "data list" that defines them.

This would be quite an exercise! How much simpler it is to arrange the computer to count off the digits, to look up in *its* memory the corresponding characters, noting the first-place ones that mark the words, and finally to print out the mnemonic words on an electric typewriter. Without some such automatic translation man's contact with the machine would be so remote, and the transfer of problems and answers to and from the machine so slow, that electronic computer technology would hardly be feasible.

Such translation from binary digits to characters and words is the product of computers. Information may be fed into the computer by an electric typewriter, which automatically translates each keyboard character into the standard code group for that character. The machine automatically inserts a zero or a one in the second place to make each code group "even." Similarly, information may be taken out of the computer, by using the same typewriter as an automatic printer, which translates the code groups from within the machine into characters, spaces, and mnemonic words.

Now, finally, what about "plain English"? So long as only mnemonic words are used to instruct and to feed information in and out, computer language is in the hands of specialists. To bring it closer to the larger worlds of science, commerce, and industry, still other translations, from and to natural language, are needed. These translations also exist, and they are also automatic. Such translation programs (called "compilers") take more complicated computer arrangements, and they take more time, than mnemonic translation. But they so vastly extend the utility of a computer system, that they are rapidly becoming as important (and as expensive to produce) as the computer equipment itself. They have a name—"software"—a general name for programming aids, of which the compiler translation is a principal jewel. We shall have more to say about software in Chapter 8.

CHAPTER 5

TWO KINDS OF LOGIC

A Hair perhaps divides the False and True.
—OMAR KHAYYÁM

In an act of human intelligence, we manipulate ideas, combining and transforming them in accordance with the logic of language. A computer, in an act of artificial intelligence, must do the same. It must combine and transform computer words in accordance with the rules of computer logic.

The science that deals with the relationships between computer words, phrases, and sentences is known as *symbolic logic*. In symbolic logic symbols and signs represent logical concepts and relations, just as in algebra letters represent numerical quantities and signs ($+$, $-$, $=$, etc.) represent relations between these quantities. In symbolic logic, as in algebra, the first letters of the alphabet (a, b, c, etc.) customarily denote *given* logical information and the last letters (x, y, z) denote *unknown* (or *dependent*) logical information. The letters may, for example, represent *logical statements*. We connect the letters with the signs of logic and thus form logical *equations,* which may be solved to find the form of the dependent statement in terms of the forms of the given statements on which it depends.

The idea of a logical equation, on first acquaintance, is strange. The mystery is dispelled when we remember that any equation, in algebra or logic, is merely a shorthand expression of ideas and their connections that can be translated readily into natural language. For example, we read the algebraic equation $x = a + b$ as "the quantity x is equal to the quantity a added to the quantity b."

In symbolic logic this equation has *two,* quite different, meanings. One translation in logic of $x = a + b$ is, "The statement x is true when, and only when, statement a is true, *or* statement b is true, *or both* are true." Another translation is, "The class x contains those elements which are members of class a *or* of class b, *or of both* class a and class b."

These two translations* of the same logical equation illustrate two forms of symbolic logic of interest in computer science. The first is "true-or-false" logic. A *true* statement is assigned the truth value 1, a *false* statement the truth value 0. In solving a logical equation, we find out whether the unknown x has the truth value 1 or 0; that is, whether x is a true or a false statement. The second is "all-or-none" logic. It deals with *classes* of ideas. The digit 1 is assigned to the class that contains all the ideas (*elements*) in a given logical discussion, whereas the

---

* The connective sign $+$ in algebra means "added to," whereas in logic $+$ means "or . . . or both." This distinction serves as a warning that the rules for manipulating algebraic quantities are not necessarily the same as those for logical statements and classes, as we shall see later in this chapter.

digit 0 represents the class that contains none of those elements. In solving for the unknown class x, we find what elements it contains from among those contained in the given classes.

By assigning the digits 1 and 0 to logical statements and classes, we transform them into a binary-digit form, suitable for digestion by a digital computer. But the larger question of *how* a computer can manipulate binary expressions to distinguish truth from falsity, or to determine likenesses and differences among classes of ideas is, at this stage, far from clear.

Fortunately, there are two devices, known as the *truth table* and the *Venn diagram,* that serve to illustrate the relationships of symbolic logic in easy-to-visualize fashion. We shall devote this chapter to development of these tables and diagrams from first principles. We shall show also the circuits that are electrical analogs of truth tables and Venn diagrams.

Tables of Truth and Falsity

First, let us examine the meaning and consequences of the logical equation $x = a$. In true-or-false logic this equation relates the truth (or falsity) of one statement with another. It may be read, "The statement x is true when, and only when, the statement a is true."

The equation is satisfied, evidently, when the statements x and a have precisely the same wording. For example, if x stands for the statement "It is raining" and a also stands for "It is raining," there is no argument about it. If one is true the other must be true and $x = a$. But the statements need not have the same wording, provided they both have the same *truth* within the context of the logical discussion of which they are a part. Thus the equation is satisfied if x is "It is raining" and a is "Drops of water are falling from clouds in the sky," since (in our context) these are equally true. But we must be careful not to equate statements that do not *necessarily* have the same truth. Thus, if a is "Drops of water are falling," the drops may be falling from a garden hose, and x is then not necessarily true when a is true.

In other words, for the equation to hold generally the statements x and a must have identical truth. Hence, this equation expresses the logical concept *identity*. The equation for identity also serves to equate false statements. Thus, if it is, in fact, not raining, the statement $x =$ "It is raining" is false, and the logically identical statement $a =$ "Drops of water are falling from clouds in the sky" is equally false. The equation $x = a$ is satisfied despite the fact that the two statements are untrue, so long as both are untrue.

Our equation thus expresses the fact that two statements having the same truth value must be both true or both false. No other true-or-false relation can exist between them. These simple, self-evident conclusions embody a profound rule-of-thought on which the equations of mathematics ultimately rest.

Now let us introduce the values for truth and falsity, 1 and 0 respectively. Our equation can be satisfied in two ways when we substitute these truth values for the statements x and a, that is $1 = 1$ and $0 = 0$. The two other possible substitutions ($0 = 1$ and $1 = 0$) violate logic (and binary arithmetic!) because they state that two statements having the same truth can be false and true respectively, and vice versa.

We may write the two relations between identical statements in tabular form as follows:

Statements	a	$x = a$	
First line of table	0	0	*Identity*
Second line of table	1	1	(x has the same truth as a)

This is the truth table for identity. It states (first line) that if any statement a is false (0) any equally true statement x is false (0), and (second line) that if any statement a is true (1) any equally true statement x is true (1). Since no other true-or-false relationship can exist between identically true or false statements there are two, and only two, lines in the table.

In the same way, we can express *negation,* the relation between two statements which are logically *opposite.* The logical equation is $x = \bar{a}$. It reads "the statement x is true when, and only when, the statement a is false." The bar over the symbol a represents the adverb "not" and $\bar{a}$ is read "not-a."

Appropriate examples are $x =$ "It is raining," $a =$ "It is not raining," and $\bar{a} =$ It is *not* not raining." The equation expresses the fact that statement x and statement $\bar{a}$ have the same truth value; that is, both are true, or both are false. This condition requires that x and a (without the bar) have opposite truth values; that is, one can be true only when the other is false.

The truth table for negation is:

Statements	a	$x = \bar{a}$	
First line	0	1	*Negation*
Second line	1	0	(x has the opposite truth of a)

The fact that there are only two lines in this table embodies the deceptively simple rule-of-thought: Logically opposite statements must be either true and false respectively, or false and true respectively. No other logical relation between them can exist.

The only other relation that one statement can have with another is logical *independence,* which occurs when the truth or falsity of one statement has nothing to do with the truth or falsity of another. The statements a = "It is raining" and x = "It is dry indoors" are an example.

We may call these two tables "single-statement" truth tables, since each has the given statement a and a dependent statement x. They represent two parts of a logical totality: between one given statement and another logically related statement three, and only three, true-or-false relations exist. These are identity, negation, and independence.

We can illustrate the electric circuits for identity and negation with the familiar wall switch (Fig. 14). When the handle of the switch is pushed up the contact within it is closed, and current flows from terminal p to terminal q. When the handle is pushed down the contact is broken and no current flows. Now let the given statement a be "The handle of the switch is up," and the dependent statement x be "Current flows from p to q." The opposite state-

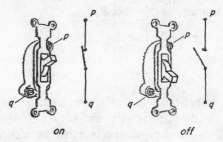

FIG. 14. The two positions of a wall switch and the respective circuit diagrams.

ments are $\bar{a}$ "The handle of the switch is down" and $\bar{x}$ "Current does not flow from p to q."

If the wall switch is installed in the wall rightside up its circuit represents identity, that is $a = x$; statement x is true if statement a is true, and statement x is false if statement a is false. To represent negation, the switch is installed upside down. Then statement $\bar{x}$ is true when statement a is true, and $\bar{x}$ is false when a is false; that is, $a = \bar{x}$.

The wall-switch circuit has two input conditions and two output conditions. These are:

Input 0	Switch handle down $(a = 0)$
Input 1	Switch handle up $(a = 1)$
Output 0	No current flow from p to q $(x = 0)$
Output 1	Current flow from p to q $(x = 1)$

Later we shall see that the switches used in computers (diodes and transistors) have an input terminal which receives a 0-voltage or a 1-voltage, and an output terminal at which appears a 0-voltage or a 1-voltage. The input and output voltages are alike for the identity circuit, unlike for the negation circuit.

84

Tables for Two Statements

Things get rapidly more interesting when we take the next step and consider *two* given statements, *a* and *b*. Let *a* be, as before, "It is raining," and let *b* = "The grass is wet." We now consider what kinds of logically dependent statements (*x*'s) can be formed from all the possible true-or-false relations between these statements. One such dependent statement is *x* = "It is raining *and* the grass is wet." The key word here is "and," the logical connective of language. The logical symbol for "and" is (·) the centered dot. It expresses the logical concept of the *conjunction* of the two statements. The logical equation is $x = a \cdot b$. Its truth table is:

Statements	a	b	$x = a \cdot b$	
First line	0	0	0	
Second line	0	1	0	*Conjunction*
Third line	1	0	0	(*x* is *a* and *b*)
Fourth line	1	1	1	

Note first that there are exactly four lines in this table—no more or less—since the two given statements *a* and *b* can be arranged in exactly four combinations of truth (1) and falsity (0). We read the table: First line, "If statements *a* and *b* are both false (both 0), then the dependent statement $x = a \cdot b$ is false (0). We can check this by writing it out in full: If it is *not* raining *and* the grass is *not* wet, then the statement "It is raining *and* the grass is wet" clearly is a false statement. Similarly, we read the second and third lines of the table, "If one given

85

statement is true and the other false, then the logically dependent statement $x = a \cdot b$ is false. *Only* when a and b are both true, can x be true, as expressed in the fourth line.

This "two-statement" truth table (there are two given statements, a and b) expresses the logical relationship of conjunction: Two statements connected by "and" make a true statement only when both are true. Otherwise they make a false statement.

The logical connective "and" between two statements denotes the bringing together ("conjunction") of two ideas. It does not mean anything else. In particular, it does not connote any cause-and-effect relation between the ideas. The statement $x =$ "It is raining *and* the grass is wet" has a different meaning, in logic, from the statement $x =$ "It is raining, *therefore* the grass is wet." The cause-and-effect connective "therefore" and its close relative "because" are represented by different two-statement truth tables, as we shall see in the following pages.

The wall-switch circuit for conjunction is shown in Fig. 15. Here we have two rightside-up wall switches, A and B. Statement a is "The handle of switch A is up"; b is "The handle of switch B is up";

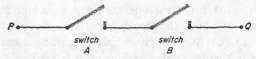

Fig. 15. Connected in series, two switches represent the truth table for "and" (conjunction). Current flows from P to Q, when and only when Switch A *and* Switch B are both closed.

and x is "Current flows from P to Q." Statement x is true only when statements *a and b* are true; that is, current flows only when both switches are closed. The input and output conditions of this circuit are:

A input 0   Switch A is open $(a = 0)$
A input 1   Switch A is closed $(a = 1)$
B input 0   Switch B is open $(b = 0)$
B input 1   Switch B is closed $(b = 1)$
Output 0   No current flows from P to Q $(x = 0)$
Output 1   Current flows from P to Q $(x = 1)$

A comparison of these conditions with the 0's and 1's from the truth table for conjunction confirms that the circuit agrees with the table in all four lines. There is no other way in which the circuit may be set. The circuit is, therefore, an exact electrical analog of the logical concept of conjunction.

The Logic of Choice

We come next to the logical concept of *choice*. To make decisions between alternatives is one of the basic operations in artificial intelligence. When we say, "*If* statement so-and-so is true, then proceed to the next instruction; *otherwise* return to instruction such-and-such," we are demanding that a choice be made between alternatives.

In logic the principal relation between alternatives is called "disjunction" and it is abbreviated by the sign +, meaning "or . . . or both." The logical equation is $x = a + b$ and it may be read in two ways that have the same logical meaning. First, "The statement x is true when statement a is true, *or* when statement b is true, *or* when *both a* and *b* are true."

87

The second rendition is, "If either statement *a or b* is true, *or* if *both a* and *b* are true, then *x* is true." Disjunction thus incorporates the functions of such important connectives in natural language as either, or, both, when, if, and then.

We can form the truth table for disjunction by inspection of the defining statements given above:

Statements	a	b	$x = a + b$	
First line	0	0	0	*Disjunction*
Second line	0	1	1	(*x* is *a* or *b*
Third line	1	0	1	or both)
Fourth line	1	1	1	

This table embodies the important concept of a truth dependent on the truth of at least one of two alternative statements.

A closely related logical concept much used in computers is the opposite of disjunction. The defining statement is: "The statement *x* is true when, and only when, both statement *a* and statement *b* are false." The equation is $x = a \downarrow b$. The table, readily formed from inspection of its definition, is:

Statements	a	b	$x = a \downarrow b$	
First line	0	0	1	
Second line	0	1	0	*Dagger*
Third line	1	0	0	(*x* is neither
Fourth line	1	1	0	*a* nor *b*)

This is called the "dagger" relation in logic, after the abbreviation $\downarrow$. We note that the digits in its *x* column are exactly the opposite of the corresponding digits in the disjunction table. For this reason it is often called the "nor" relation, the prefixed "n" before "or" meaning "the logical opposite of."

The wall-switch circuit for disjunction is shown in Fig. 16. There are two rightside-up switches con-

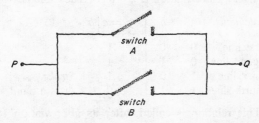

FIG. 16. Connected in parallel, two switches represent "or . . . or both" (disjunction). Current flows when either Switch A *or* Switch B is closed, *or both* are closed.

nected "in parallel." The statements and the input-output conditions are the same as listed on page 87. If we compare the operation of this circuit with the table for disjunction, we find it agrees with each line in the table and that there is no other way of setting the circuit. The circuit therefore is the exact electrical analog of disjunction: Current flows when either switch A or switch B is closed, or both are closed.

To represent the logical opposite of disjunction, the "nor" relation, we use the same circuit (Fig. 16), the same statements, and the same input/output conditions. But we place both switches in the wall *upside down*. Comparison of the operation of this circuit with the dagger (nor) truth table reveals that it is the exact electrical analog. In diode and transistor circuits, we get the effect of turning the switch upside down by interchanging the 0 and 1 input terminals, as we shall see in Chapter 6, or by inter-posing a negation circuit.

Still another logical relation used in computers is "the statement x is true when either a or b, or both, is false." The equation is $x = a \mid b$. The table is:

Statements	a	b	$x = a \mid b$	
First line	0	0	1	
Second line	0	1	1	
Third line	1	0	1	*Stroke*
Fourth line	1	1	0	(x is a nand b)

This relation is called, after its abbreviation ($\mid$), the "stroke." Its x column is the exact opposite of that of the conjunction ("and") table. So it is often called "nand."

The circuit for the *nand* relation is the same as that for *and* (Fig. 15), except that both switches are upside down. This latter arrangement reverses the logic, as it must, since *nand* is the logical opposite of *and*.

Cause and Effect

Next comes an important question. What is the logic of cause-and-effect? What about the powerful connectives of natural language "because" and "therefore"? We have dealt with this subject already (but not in so many words) in the table for disjunction, for example. This treats statements of the type, "If a is true, or b is true, or if both are true, then x is true." In many situations, the truth of a or b, or both, may represent the *cause* of x's being true. That is, we may say, "x is true *because* a is true, or *be-*

cause b is true, or *because* both are true." Or we may reverse the English and say: "Since *x* is true, *therefore a* must be true, or *b* must be true, or both must be true." Disjunction thus provides a framework for "because" and "therefore." These connections may, in fact, be inserted in the defining statements of other truth tables.

For our final truth table, which illustrates an important example of cause-and-effect logic, we take up the logical idea that *"a implies b."* The logical statement for this relation, called "material implication," is: *x* is true when either *a* is false, or *b* is true. The equation is $x = a \rightarrow b$. This bald statement is hard to understand, although the truth table can be readily drawn up from it:

Statements	*a*	*b*	$x = a \rightarrow b$	
First line	0	0	1	
Second line	0	1	1	
Third line	1	0	0	*Material Impli-*
Fourth line	1	1	1	*cation* (*x* is *a* implies *b*)

This table represents a one-way logical pathway. As in our previous example, we take *a* = "It is raining" and *b* = "The grass is wet." The one-way implication between rain and wet grass then takes the general form, "The fact that it is raining necessarily implies that the grass is wet, but wet grass does not necessarily imply that it is raining" (a garden hose can produce wet grass, but the grass cannot remain dry if it is raining).

Thus, if it is not raining it is true that the grass may be dry (line 1) or wet (from some other wetting agent or a previous rainfall, line 2). But if it is raining the grass must be wet. This condition makes x false in line 3, which says "Rain implies dry grass" and x true in line 4, which says "Rain implies wet grass."

This is a long way around to say, "Rain necessarily implies wet grass, but wet grass does not necessarily imply rain." The symbol for material implication, the arrow, points from cause on the left to effect on the right: $a \rightarrow b$, and (in the cause-and-effect context) it reads, "a is the cause of b, but b is not the cause of a."

The circuit for material implication is that shown in Fig. 16, but switch A is *upside down*. Otherwise the circuit, its statements and input/output conditions are the same as those of Fig. 16. Comparison of this circuit with the table for material implication shows that it is the exact electrical analog. To change the logic of a computer circuit from disjunction to material implication, then, we need only interchange the 0 and 1 input terminals of switch A.

How Many Truth Tables Are There?

One of the central questions in designing computers and in devising programs of computation is: How many truth tables are there? If there are only a few, we can plan to use an electrical analog (like those in Figs. 15 and 16) to represent each type; and we can devise a program that tests the logical connections of the computation in terms of each truth table, one after the other, until all the possibilities have been examined. But if the number of truth tables is large, these straightforward procedures might be impractical. The astonishing fact is that in even simple logical problems, in which several given statements as a group are considered for all their logical relations, the number of truth tables becomes astronomically large. Whenever four or more statements are to be examined as a group for their logical relations (and this sometimes happens even in simple problems), one cannot proceed by systematic logic alone because the numbers get too big.† The computer would be impossibly expensive, and the time to complete an exhaustive examination of all the logical possibilities would be impossibly long. Instead, the problem must be broken down into subproblems, involving only two or three statements each, and common sense must select the logical pathway from one sub-problem to the next.

The use of common sense in problem solving, as contrasted to formal logic, is a form of "impure" mathematics known as *heuristics*. In heuristics, we devise rules, based in large part on our natural processes of reasoning, which experience tells us represent significant and useful relations in the real world. Heuristicians are, of course, logical, but they are also inventive, clever, and the best ones are brilliant. Moreover, heuristicians, like Archimedes in the bathtub, are continually being surprised by the significance of evidence previously ignored. Heuristics uses any tool, logic included, that comes to hand. Its results depend, in varying degrees, on experience, luck, educated guesswork, serendipity, inspiration,

† The number of different truth tables, when N different statements are arranged in all possible combinations of truth and falsity is $2^{(2^N)}$. For five statements, this is 2^{32} or 4,294,967,296 different truth tables! To represent these electrically would require 1,228,158 different electrical circuits.

and courage. Computer intelligence does not depend on logic alone; it owes an overwhelming debt to heuristics—another way of saying that intelligent machinery can be built and programmed only in imitation of the natural processes of thought. Any attempt to strike off into the wilderness of even five-statement relations by logic alone is utterly without reward.

The Logic of All-or-None

Having set up the tables of true-or-false logic which can be imitated in the circuits of a computer, we must now examine a different set of meanings of the digits 0 and 1: Suppose we say 0 means "none" and 1 means "all." This is quite a different pair of concepts from "false" and "true," but the relations between "all" and "none" have the same form. We can use the same electric circuits not only to deal with truth and falsity, but also to distinguish *classes* of ideas. The digit 1 can represent the most general class, that is, *all* the elements in a given set of ideas, and 0 can represent *no* elements in that set of ideas.

This system of thought (called the *algebra of classes*) can be illustrated in consideration of the part of speech called a noun. Each noun, you will recall, represents a general class of things having something in common; the various definitions in the dictionary represent subclasses, the words in the definitions being in themselves subclasses of the subclasses. Evidently, if we are to represent the complications of natural language in computer circuits and programs, we must arrange for the computer to deal with echelons of classes and subclasses.

The "Whirling Dervish" of Chapter 1 is a device based on class logic.

To illustrate the logical relationships between classes, let us consider the noun "student" as it relates to a particular school, Abington South Campus High School, in suburban Philadelphia. This school is chosen because its division into just two grades, junior and senior, makes Fig. 20 much easier to draw. (This school, incidentally, was one of the first to acquire an electronic digital computer for instruction in computer science.)

The most general class of students in this school is $1 = all$ the students in Abington South Campus High. The other end of the logical spectrum is $0 = no$ students in Abington South Campus High.

Between these limits we can identify some subclasses:

All the male students
All the female students
The male students in the senior class
The female students in the senior class
The male students in the junior class
The female students in the junior class
The students on the football squad
The students on the field hockey squad
The students in the honor society
The students on the debating team

We see that the male and female classes are separate, but that overlaps occur between subclasses in sports and honors, with respect to the male-female and junior-senior distinctions. How do we represent the relations among these subclasses?

The Venn Diagram

For this sort of graphical representation we are well served by the diagrams suggested by the British logician John Venn (1834–1923). Points on a Venn diagram represent the elementary concepts (*elements*) in a logical discussion. In our case we can put down a point for each student. All the points within the whole area of the diagram represent (Fig. 17) the general class 1 = *all* the students in Abington

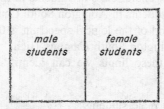

FIG. 17. A Venn diagram representing the class of "all students." The two halves represent major subclasses, the boys and the girls.

South Campus High. Points in a portion of the area, then, represent the elements of a subclass. Thus in Fig. 17 the male and female students are distinct subclasses. Together they fill up the whole diagram, since together they constitute all the students. We can further divide each of the subclasses (Fig. 18) into smaller ones, such as the football squad, which is all-male, and the field hockey team, which is all-female.

We can also show classes that are part male, part female, like the honor students and the debating

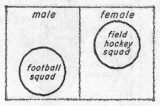

FIG. 18. Subclasses within subclasses. The football squad is composed wholly of boys, the field hockey squad wholly of girls.

team, which overlap the boundary between the boys and girls (Fig. 19). Since some debaters are honor students there is a further overlap, as shown. We can show also that there is no student who is both a football player and a debater (no overlap between these subclasses). Finally, if we consider the participation in sports and honors by junior classmen as against seniors, we can get a very complicated diagram (Fig. 20).

We can draw boundaries around the outlines of several subclasses to form larger subclasses, and in this way we can represent the logical relations of "not" and "and" and "or" and so on. Thus, the

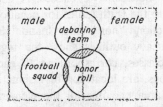

FIG. 19. Overlaps between subclasses, shown shaded. A few football players are on the honor roll, but none has time to devote to debating.

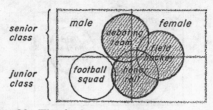

FIG. 20. The junior and senior classes. In this hypothetical example, the junior class has most of the athletes and bright students, whereas the seniors are great talkers. The heavy outline shows how subclasses may be combined. The shaded area within this boundary represents the students who participate in debating, hockey, or honors, or in two or three of these activities.

heavy boundary in Fig. 20 encloses the subclasses of students who are either debaters or field hockey players or honor students, as well as students who participate in two or more of these activities (in the overlap areas)—for example, those who are debaters and honor students. The points on the diagram outside the heavy outline represent the students who do not participate in any of these sports or honors.

To make these relations clear, we show in Fig. 21 the relations between two classes, A and B, which correspond to the truth tables for negation, conjunction, disjunction, "nor," and "nand." The shaded areas and heavy outlines show the regions within which the classes, corresponding to each of these logical notions, are located. For disjunction, for example, the area encloses all the elements that are either in A *or* B, or in *both* A and B. The shading of the "nor" diagram is the reverse of disjunction, and "nand" is the reverse of conjunction. The elec-

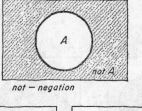

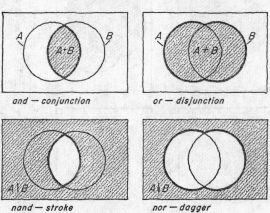

Fig. 21. Five logical relations shown in Venn diagram. The shaded areas show the elements of the classes formed by the corresponding logical equations.

trical analogs of these Venn diagrams are given in Figs. 15 and 16. It is apparent that these circuits can be used as well for class logic as for true-or-false logic.

To summarize, the connective words of language express logical relationships between ideas. These relations may be represented by truth tables or by class diagrams, both of which can be represented electrically in the circuits of a computer. To avoid

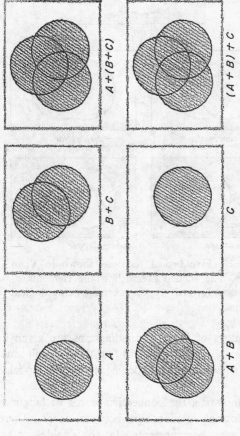

Fig. 22. Combination of classes by "or . . . or both" (+) in any order. In this example, the shape of the class for A + (B+C) is the same as that for (A+B) + C.

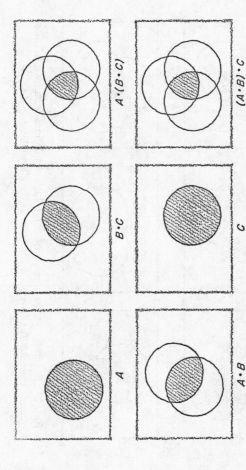

FIG. 23. Combination of classes by "and" (·) in any order. The shaded areas show that classes A · (B·C) and (A·B) · C are identical.

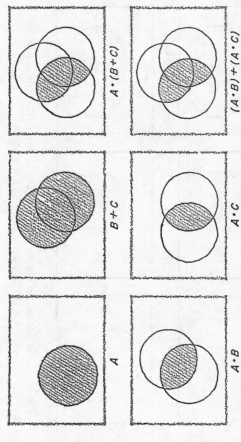

FIG. 24. Resemblance to algebra of some logical relations is shown in these diagrams; the class A · (B+C) is the same as the class (A·B) + (A·C).

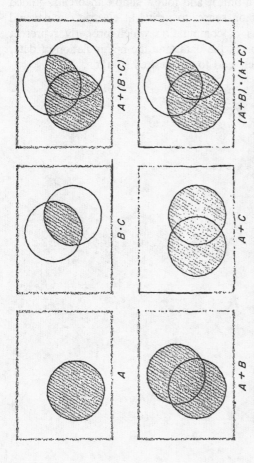

A

A + B

B · C

A + C

A + (B · C)

(A+B) · (A+C)

FIG. 25. Difference from algebra of most logical relations is illustrated in these examples: in logic the class A + (B·C) is the same as the class (A+B) · (A+C).

impossibly complicated associations of many ideas at once, we combine them two-at-a-time (or at worst three-at-a-time), and follow simple theorems, guided by common sense, to arrive at electric circuits and programs of computation which properly represent the problem, the data, and the manipulation of data, and which lead to the desired solution.

CHAPTER 6

DIODES, TRANSISTORS, AND CORES

Ere the parting hour go by
Quick thy tablets, Memory!
—SIR EDWARD ARNOLD

The devices used as switches in computers are diodes and transistors.* They operate at prodigious speed. A typical high-speed switching transistor can close or open in a few billionths of a second. Pairs of transistors are used also as memory cells for storing numbers temporarily—to hold the addend and augend bits during addition, for example.

For storing instructions and data over longer periods, magnetic devices are used. Depending on the direction of their magnetic lines of force they store a 0 or a 1. Storage of numbers during a computer program is accomplished with tiny doughnut-shaped *cores* of magnetic material, one for each bit to be stored. Magnetic tape is used for longer storage. Bits may also be stored in mechanical form, as holes

---

* The checker-playing 7094 computer has 5700 diodes, 44,000 transistors, 1,152,000 memory cores, and 66,500 other electrical circuit components!

which are punched (for 1's) or not punched (for 0's) in cards or paper tape.

Switches and memory cells perform two functions. First, they must be able to accept a bit; that is, respond to either of two input conditions, 0 or 1. Second, they must be able to furnish a bit; that is, provide either of two output conditions, 0 or 1. A switch arranged for negation passes an output opposite to its input. Switches connected for binary addition must accept the carry, addend, and augend bits as inputs, and provide the sum bit and the next carry bit as outputs. A set of eight memory cores (arranged to store an eight-bit character in Model 1401 language) must accept the bits of the character to be stored as inputs and provide as outputs the same eight bits when the character is retrieved from memory.

To transfer information, one device is connected to another, the output from the first serving as the input to the second. Thus, when a digit is to be stored, the transistor that provides the digit as an output is connected to the appropriate magnetic core, which accepts the digit as an input and stores it. Later, when the program calls for that digit to be used in the computation, the core provides a bit, as an output, to the appropriate diode or transistor, which accepts the digit as an input.

Diodes: One-way Conductors

The simplest computer switch is the diode. It is a one-way conductor: electric current passes readily through it in one direction only. (The current that can pass in the opposite direction is so small we can call it zero for all practical purposes.) The one-way character of the diode is shown in its circuit symbol (Fig. 26), a bar and an arrow. The arrow is the

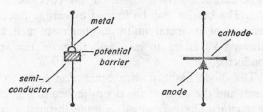

FIG. 26. Semiconductor diode and its circuit symbol.

positive electrode or anode and it indicates the easy direction of the flow of current through the device. The bar represents the cathode, or negative electrode. If the positive terminal of a source of voltage (battery or d.c. power supply) is connected to the anode, negative to the cathode, current flows. If the connections are reversed, no current flows. Diodes permit current to flow whenever the anode is more positive than the cathode, but not otherwise.

Diodes exhibit this behavior by virtue of the electrical properties of semiconductors and metals. A semiconductor is a material that can conduct electricity, but not very well. The element silicon is the semiconductor most used in computer diodes. Compared with copper, silicon is a poor conductor, but compared with an insulator like porcelain it is a very good conductor. This in-between ability to carry electricity is only of incidental interest. More significant is the fact that when a semiconductor is brought into contact with a particular metal, such as

107

gallium, a potential barrier appears at the boundary between the semiconductor and the metal. This barrier prevents electrons from passing in one direction while permitting them to pass in the opposite direction. The barrier may be formed by raising the temperature of the metal until it just begins to melt, thus allowing its atoms to mix with those of the semiconductor.

The diode has two wire connections, one to the metal and the other to the opposite face of the semiconductor. The two wires protrude through a coating of glass or other protective material.

The output of a diode is developed by passing its current through an electrical resistance, across which a voltage appears when the current flows. The elementary diode circuit is shown in Fig. 27. When a

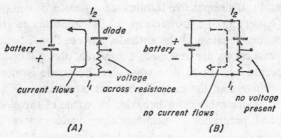

FIG. 27. Elementary diode circuit. A voltage appears across the resistance, only when the anode of the diode is made more positive than its cathode, that is, when current flows. If the cathode is made more positive, no current flows and no output voltage appears.

positive voltage is applied (Fig. 27-A) to the anode through the input terminal I_1 (negative voltage to the cathode via input terminal I_2), current flows and a voltage appears across the resistance. When the battery is reversed (Fig. 27-B), making the anode more negative, no current flows and no voltage appears across the output terminals.

In the conducting condition a diode can carry not only the current produced by its input voltage but also a current fed from another circuit. The diode can thus control other circuits. So used, it is called a "diode gate," since it passes information when conducting, holds back information when non-conducting. In a typical gate circuit, a diode is connected between the output of the machine memory and the augend section (*augend register*) of the adder. When a stored augend is to be passed to the adder, the control unit applies a positive voltage to the diode's anode. The diode conducts, and connects the memory to the adder. At completion of the transfer of the augend the diode resumes its nonconducting state, disconnecting the memory and protecting the augend register from any further disturbance. Another diode is caused then to connect the addend register to the memory to transfer the addend. When the adder produces the sum, still another diode conducts and transfers the sum back to the memory.

In this manner, information may be routed from any part of the computer to any other part, through diodes which pass bits or inhibit their passage as the control unit directs. Note particularly that a diode gate has two equally important duties: to pass information when called upon, and to see that no information is passed at other times. It must be able to isolate as well as connect.

109

Diodes are used also as switches in logic circuits. An example is the disjunction ("or . . . or both") circuit, shown in Fig. 28. As the truth table for dis-

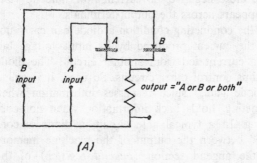

(A)

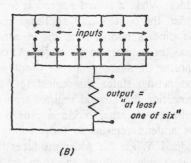

(B)

FIG. 28. Diode circuits for "or . . . or both." (A) An output appears when either input A or input B or both is present. (B) Six diodes may be connected to form the output when "at least one of six inputs is present."

junction shows, a 1-output is required whenever there is at least one 1-input. Two diodes connected to a common output resistance serve for two inputs (Fig. 28-A). If a 1-input is applied to either or both, current flows through the resistance, and a 1-output is produced. This scheme can be extended to accept many inputs, the respective diodes feeding a common output resistance (Fig. 28-B). This "or" circuit will produce a 1-output whenever a 1-input is presented to at least one of the diodes. The isolation function of the diode is particularly important in this circuit. Each diode can pass current only to the common output resistance; backward flow to the other input circuits is prevented by the one-way-only property of the other diodes.

The logic of conjunction ("and") can be performed similarly by any number of diodes connected in series (Fig. 29). Each diode is made separately

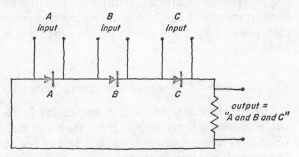

FIG. 29. Diode circuit for "and." If any input is absent, there is no output.

conducting by its individual 1-input (making the anode positive or the cathode negative). Only when all the diodes have a 1-input is the circuit completed. Then current flows through the output resistance, producing a 1-output. If any of the diodes is not conducting, a 0-output is produced.

Diodes can be interconnected to perform all the

functions of logic, and in recent computers diodes are in fact used for the majority of logic and control operations. They are cheaper than transistors and operate at about the same speed, but they have certain limitations. First, the diode circuit inevitably consumes a part of the input voltage (which is divided between the diode and the output resistor). When several diode circuits are used in cascade, one feeding the next, the output voltage of one of the diodes in the chain may become so low that it cannot serve as the input for the next, and *amplification* is needed. The transistor, being an amplifier in itself, escapes this problem. Moreover, the diode is not a storage device; when its input is removed its output vanishes. Individual transistors lack storage, but two transistors can be interconnected to amplify each other's output and store a bit after the input is removed.

The Transistor—A Diode with an Extra Connection

The transistor is a device that can amplify its input, producing a larger output. It has three terminals (Fig. 30). If input power is applied to any two of its terminals a larger amount of power can be taken from the third terminal and either of the other two. Physically, a transistor is the equivalent of two diodes connected back-to-back. The diodes are formed on opposite faces of a single piece of a semiconductor (again, silicon is used in most computer transistors, although germanium is used in many).

Two kinds of current-carrying charges can be used in transistors, electrons and holes. The "hole"†

† See *Perpetual Motion,* by Alec T. Stewart (Doubleday & Company, Science Study Series, 1965).

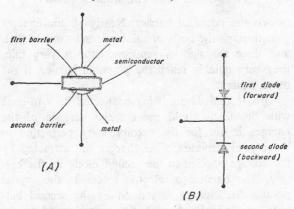

first barrier   metal

semiconductor

second barrier   metal

(A)

first diode
(forward)

second diode
(backward)

(B)

FIG. 30. Transistor and its equivalent circuit (two diodes "back-to-back").

is actually the absence of an electron in the outer shell of an atom of the semiconductor. As electrons are lost and picked up by the atoms, the vacancy "moves," and the hole thus has the properties of a moving positive particle.

One of the diodes of the transistor serves to accept the input. It is connected to a battery which makes the anode positive, allowing a steady current to flow across the diode's potential barrier. The input voltage, applied in series with the battery, causes the current to be increased or decreased depending on the polarity of the input.

The semiconductor of which the transistor is made is a crystal whose structure is as nearly perfect as modern technology can achieve. Because of the balance of the electrical forces among the atoms of the near-perfect crystals, the atoms cannot easily capture the current-carrying charges after they have

113

passed the potential barrier. Nearly all the charges pass through the body of the semiconductor, in fact, and since the slab of semiconductor is very thin, they very quickly reach the potential barrier of the other diode.

This second diode, being connected back-to-back with the first, would prevent the passage of the charges if not for the extraordinary perfection of the crystal structure. The charges are attracted by the voltage applied to the second diode by the battery. The balance of electric forces in the crystal permits the charges, urged on by the second battery, to "tunnel" through the second barrier, and they reach the outside world through the third terminal of the transistor.

How does amplification occur? The answer is to be found in the difference in the electrical resistance of the two diodes. The first diode, you recall, passes current in the "easy" direction; a small change in input voltage will produce a large change in the current passing the first barrier. When the current passes through the second barrier, it encounters a much higher resistance, since the second diode impedes the current flow. In the passage through this higher resistance, the changes in the current produce changes in voltage (at the output) which are comparatively large, an amplified version of the input.

The circuit symbol for the transistor is shown in Fig. 31. The arrow represents the *emitter,* which injects the current-carrying charges through the first barrier. The vertical line represents the body of the semiconductor; it is called the *base.* The slanting line represents the *collector,* which collects the charges after they have passed the second barrier.

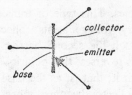

FIG. 31. Circuit symbol of the transistor.

The output of the transistor is developed by passing the collected current through a resistance, across which the output voltage appears.

Transistors can be used in three basic circuits depending on which two of the three terminals accept the input. The circuit most widely used (Fig. 32) is called the common emitter circuit because its emitter is common to its input and output. In our illustrative circuit we use the so-called "P-N-P" type of transistor, in which the current-carrying charges

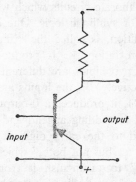

FIG. 32. Common emitter transistor circuit. In this circuit the polarity of the output is the reverse of its input, so it performs the logic of "not" (negation).

115

are positive holes. This type of transistor requires a negative battery voltage at its collector, to attract the holes through the second barrier. The common emitter circuit reverses the polarity of any signal passing through it; that is, as the base is made more positive, the collector becomes more negative. This circuit thus performs the "negation" function in logic.

Like diodes, two transistors may be connected to a common output resistance (Fig. 33-A) to perform "or . . . or both" logic. Several transistors with a common output resistance perform "at least one of many" logic. Transistors connected in series perform "and" logic. In Fig. 33-B, if every transistor has a 1-input, current will flow through the output resistance to produce a 1-output.

The circuits for "negation," "or . . . or both," and "and" may be used as building blocks to construct more elaborate circuits which will perform all the functions of symbolic logic. One of these, used in binary addition, is called the "ring-sum" circuit after the abbreviation $\oplus$. It produces a 1-output only when its two inputs are different (0 and 1, or 1 and 0 respectively). If the inputs are alike (1 and 1, or 0 and 0), it produces a 0-output. This is the circuit needed for adding augend and addend digits without regard to the carry digit. It performs the logic of "or . . . but not both," which is known as "exclusive or" to distinguish it from disjunction, which is "inclusive or" ("or . . . or both").

One way of constructing the "exclusive or" circuit is shown in Fig. 34. The inputs A and B are reversed to $\bar{A}$ and $\bar{B}$ by the negation circuits. The two "and" circuits produce $\bar{A} \cdot B$ and $A \cdot \bar{B}$ respectively as

116

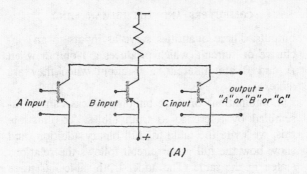

(A)

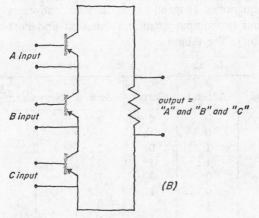

(B)

Fig. 33. Transistor circuits for ". . . or . . . or . . . or two or three of these" (A); ". . . and . . . and . . ." (B).

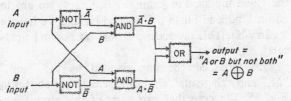

Fig. 34. Circuit for "exclusive or" (the ring-sum relationship), which produces an output when its two inputs are unlike, but not when both are alike.

outputs. These quantities serve as inputs to an "inclusive or" circuit, which produces a 1-output when A and B are different, a 0-output when they are alike.

Combinations of these building blocks can be assembled by reference to truth tables. To illustrate this, we write the table for full binary addition, and show how the full adder circuit follows the relations stated in the table. The adder truth table has three input quantities (augend-bit, addend-bit, and carry-bit) and two output quantities (sum-bit and next-carry bit). The table is:

	Inputs			Outputs
a Augend	b Addend	c Carry	Sum	Next Carry
0	0	0	0	0
0	0	1	1	0
0	1	0	1	0
0	1	1	0	1
1	0	0	1	0
1	0	1	0	1
1	1	0	0	1
1	1	1	1	1

We can read each line of the table to satisfy ourselves that the proper outputs are associated with the given inputs. For example, in line 4, we are to add a 1 addend-bit to a 0 augend-bit and we have a 1 carry-bit. This produces a 0 sum-bit and a 1 next-carry bit.

This table can be implemented by the "and," "or," and "ring-sum" circuits assembled as shown in Fig. 35. We note that two parts of this circuit, enclosed in dashed lines, are alike. These are "half-

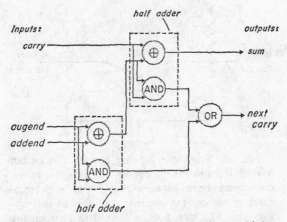

FIG. 35. Typical binary adder circuit, combining the "and" and "ring-sum" functions of two "half-adder" circuits. It produces the sum and carry digits from the augend, addend, and previous carry digits.

adders" (see Fig. 10). The "or" circuit at the right produces the next carry.

The Transistor Flip-Flop

One of the most important computer transistor circuits is the flip-flop, which stores a bit. The flip-flop is the high-speed electrical equivalent of a toggle switch. If pushed hard enough one way, it suddenly flips over and stores a bit; then, if pushed hard enough in the opposite direction it flips back and stores the opposite bit. It employs two transistors, the output of each connected to the input of the other, as shown in Fig. 36. Each transistor, being in a common emitter circuit, has an output that is the

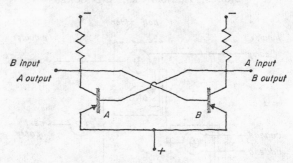

FIG. 36. Transistor flip-flop circuit. The output of each transistor is the opposite of its input, so the cross-connections between them force each transistor to assume the opposite condition of its partner. The digit stored shifts from 0 to 1, when the input 1 is transferred from transistor A to transistor B.

reverse of its input. Hence, when one transistor receives a 1-input it reverses this to a 0-output and applies the 0-output to the input of the other. The latter reverses the 0-input to a 1-output and applies this to the input of the first. This is the condition first assumed, so the circuit "locks up," one transistor reinforcing the condition of the other indefinitely. The circuit thus stores a bit (which for definiteness we may identify with the input condition of the first transistor, namely, a 1-bit).

To store a 0-bit in this circuit we apply a 1-input to the *second* transistor. This transistor converts this input to a 0-bit, applies it to the first transistor which converts it to a 1-bit and applies it to the second, as first assumed. Now the circuit is "locked" again, but the conditions of the transistors are reversed. The input condition of the first transistor is now a 0-bit, and this bit is stored indefinitely. We can detect whether a 1-bit or a 0-bit is stored by measuring the input of the first transistor.

If two auxiliary transistors are used to feed the inputs to the flip-flop (Fig. 37) we isolate its inputs

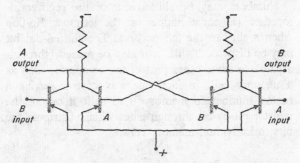

FIG. 37. Two additional transistors may be added to the flip-flop circuit to isolate its inputs.

from its outputs. We then can store readily either a 0 or a 1, and determine which is stored, without disturbing the setting of the circuit.

The output "reading" of one flip-flop may be transferred, through a diode or transistor gate, to another. This transfer is particularly useful in shifting binary numbers, as in multiplication and division. A number of flip-flops are set up in line, one for each digit in the number to be stored. Through their respective inputs, each flip-flop can be set to store 0 or 1 to represent the respective digits. Then, to shift the number one place to the left, we pass the condition of each flip-flop through a gate to its neighbor on the left. The settings of the flip-flops may then be changed (for example, by subtracting a remainder to produce a new dividend), and the

121

result then shifted again (as in binary long division, page 43). Such collections of flip-flops are called registers. They are used to hold or shift bits while they are being subjected to the operations of arithmetic.

Numbers may be shifted out of the register altogether (as must happen at the leftmost flip-flop when a shift to the left occurs). The shifted-out bit may be dispensed with, or it may be passed (through a gate) to some other part of the computer, such as a memory cell. In fact, one way of transferring a binary number to memory is to shift it out of the register bit-by-bit through gates which distribute the bits to individual memory cells.

Memory Cores

Now let us look at a magnetic memory cell, the toroidal memory core. The toroidal core, shown in Fig. 38, is made of finely powdered iron oxide with additions of magnesium oxide and manganese oxide. The powder is mixed with a binder, pressed into the shape shown, and baked to hold the shape. The cores are very small, only a few hundredths of an inch in diameter. Hundreds of thousands of them can be packed, in ordered layers, in less than a cubic foot of space.

The magnetic powder of which these cores are made has carefully been developed to have the following properties: (1) it can be permanently magnetized in either of two conditions, with the magnetic lines of force running clockwise (which we take here to represent the digit 1); or counterclockwise (the digit 0); (2) its magnetism may be re-

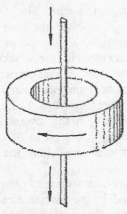

FIG. 38. Toroidal memory core and its magnetizing wire. Downward current causes clockwise magnetization; upward current, counterclockwise.

versed, changing its stored digit from 0 to 1 and vice versa, rapidly and repeatedly without deterioration; and (3) its direction of permanent magnetism, once established, can be reversed only when the reversing force exceeds a certain limit (that is, the core "hangs on" to its established magnetic direction, like the handle of the toggle switch, until it receives a sufficient push to reverse itself). A small current (of the order of a few thousandths of an ampere) passing along a wire threaded through the hole of the core establishes the magnetism. By the "right-hand rule" of electromagnetism, the lines of magnetic force run clockwise (digit 1) when the current flows *down* (this is the conventional flow of current, in the direction from the positive to the negative terminal of a battery).

Now, suppose we pass the necessary current

downward through the wire. The current must be large enough to "saturate" the core material; that is, to cause essentially all the atoms in the core to line up, magnetically, in the clockwise direction. When the current stops, the magnetism remains (the core is a "permanent magnet"), and the core then "permanently" stores the digit 1. If small amounts of current later flow in the reverse direction (up) the core stubbornly holds on to its clockwise magnetism, and protects indefinitely the storage of its digit 1.

When, however, a sufficiently large amount of current is passed in the reverse direction (upward through the wire) the magnetism suddenly reverses. The reversing current must be large enough to reverse the magnetic alignment of substantially all the atoms in the core. The core then is saturated in the counterclockwise direction, and it stores the digit 0. When the upward current stops, the core maintains its 0-bit condition until a sufficiently large downward current forces it to reverse.

In this way, we can impose either a 1 or a 0, on a magnetic core by the passage of a sufficiently large current downward or upward, respectively, through the wire threaded through the core. We can thus "write" on the "tablets of memory." But we recall that we must also *take* information from the memory unit; we must also be able to "read" from its tablets. How is this done?

When lines of magnetic force change (either in numbers or direction or both), a current is "induced" in a wire surrounded by the lines of force. Thus, if another fine wire ("sensing wire") passes through the hole of the core, a current will be induced in that wire in one direction whenever the core magnetism reverses from clockwise to counterclockwise, and the induced current will be in the reverse direction when the magnetism reverses from counterclockwise to clockwise. This sensing wire thus receives a 1 indication of the digit stored whenever the core magnetism is reversed from 1 to 0, and it receives a 0 indication when the core reverses from 0 to 1.

We can "read" a core only by changing its storage; we must, in other words, destroy the storage in the act of reading it. This defect (called "destructive read-out") is fundamental and takes special remedial measures. To replace the digit correctly after a reading requires extra circuits in the memory unit. When we "write" a digit on a core, we automatically erase a previously stored opposite digit, as indeed we must if the writing is to be correct. Suppose we wish to write a 1, and the core is already magnetized in the 1 direction. Since substantially all the atoms of the core are already lined up in the correct direction, no significant change occurs and the 1 is retained and stored, as intended. But, if the core had previously stored a 0, the 1 writing current need only be large enough to reverse the magnetism, and the 0 is replaced by a 1, as intended.

Storage of Characters and Words

So much for the storage of an individual bit. How about the storage of a character composed of several digits? Suppose we want to store the single-character mnemonic word *C,* for "compare." The italicization indicates that this is the first (in this case, the only) character in the word. From Chapter 4, we know that the standard code group for *C* (in Model 1401 language) is 11110011. To store this character we need eight cores, and we arrange these as shown in Fig. 39, one above the other, the top-

FIG. 39. Stack of memory cores magnetized to represent the character 11110011 (the character *C* in Model 1401 code).

most core corresponding to the leftmost digit. Through each core a "writing" wire is threaded. To store *C* we would pass downward (1) currents through the upper four and the lower two writing wires, and upward (0) currents through the remaining two wires.

This seems simple enough. We need one writing wire for each core, and these are fed the 1 or 0 currents, as needed, by transistors connected to them. For reading we could use an additional sensing wire in each core, the currents induced in them being fed to transistors which amplify and pass them on to the other units of the computer. Since there are tens of thousands of cores in even a small memory unit, this arrangement would require twenties of thousands of transistors, and this would be very expensive. So computer designers long ago looked for a better answer and found it in an important invention of the great French mathematician and philosopher René Descartes (1596–1650).

Suppose we have an 8½ by 11 sheet of graph paper, with lines spaced a quarter inch. There are 34 lines across the paper, 44 lines from top to bottom, and the lines intersect at $34 \times 44 = 1496$ points. To locate any one of these points, we could label each by an individual number from 1 to 1496. Or, as Descartes first suggested, we can locate any intersection by a two-number label composed of its Cartesian coordinates (its X-coordinate and its Y-coordinate). Now, instead of 1496 labels, we need only $34 + 44 = 78$ labels—a very significant simplification indeed.

To apply the same system to memory cores, we can arrange several hundred of them equally spaced in any array patterned after the intersections of our graph paper. Through the cores we thread *one* writing wire for each row and *one* writing wire for each column of the array. Suppose we want to write a digit on the core at the intersection of the 7th column and the 5th row (Fig. 40). We pass half the

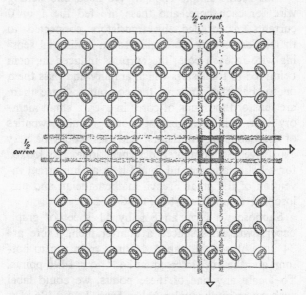

FIG. 40. Plane array of memory cores. With half the writing current passed through the fifth row and half through the seventh column, the core at the intersection receives the full current and stores a digit. The other cores in the row and column remain unaffected since half the current is insufficient to affect their magnetism.

current required to write the digit through the 7th-column wire and the other half through the 5th-row wire. The core at the intersection then receives two halves of the required current, and (since the magnetic forces add when the cores are oriented as

128

shown in Fig. 40) this combination constitutes the whole current required. The magnetism of this core is reinforced or reversed, as required, to store the bit. All the other cores in that column and that row receive only half the required writing current, remaining unaffected and continuing to store the bits they hold. Why the "toggle-switch" action of the core material is so important now becomes apparent. By this method, we reduce the number of wires and transistors required to write on any given core from tens of thousands to hundreds. Moreover, we simplify the problem of *addressing* a particular core.

Placing cores in arrays has an even greater effect in simplifying the reading of information. We need thread *one* sensing wire through all the cores, in crisscross fashion. Then to read the core, say, at the 5th-row, 7th-column address, we reverse its magnetism by exciting the corresponding write wires, and the sense wire has induced in it a "read" current derived from that core only, all the other cores remaining inactive at the time. Having read the digit, we must restore the proper direction of magnetism to that core, by writing it in again via the 5th-row, 7th-column write wires. By these means we can write a digit onto, or read a digit from, any specified core by exciting two wires that uniquely pass through that core.

The cores of a memory unit may be assembled in many horizontal arrays of cores, one above the other, such that the columns and rows of each array are aligned with those of the array above and below it. In the Model 1401 Computer, which uses eight bits for each character, we need eight arrays of cores. A character is stored in the vertical direction

129

(as in Fig. 39), in a "stack" of eight cores, each occupying the same row and column in its arrays. To address any specified character by its row and column, we excite the sixteen transistors connected to the wires through the specified row and column in the eight arrays. By exciting several row-and-column addresses, we can store a number of characters, in adjacent stacks of cores. Thus, instruction words or data words are packed into the arrays of cores, each digit in one core, each character in a vertical stack of eight cores, and each word in as many adjacent stacks as the word has characters.

Reading and writing on a memory core takes much more time than a logic circuit takes to handle a bit. Hence, one of the principal tasks of computer engineers has been to speed up the writing and reading of memory cores. Great progress has been made, but the memory action, per bit read or written, is still roughly one hundred times slower than the logic action, per bit processed. This sluggish pace is caused fundamentally by the need to align all the atoms in the core. To speed up the process memory elements having fewer atoms are needed, and ultra-thin magnetic films are beginning to replace cores in memory units.

CHAPTER 7

HARDWARE AND INFORMATION

In the popular conception, a computer is a high-speed number calculator. This view is only partly correct. A digital computer is, in fact, a general symbol-processing device, capable of performing any well-defined process for the manipulation and transformation of information.

—E. A. FEIGENBAUM AND JULIAN FELDMAN

Now we are ready to see how computer hardware, the "works" of a computer system, accepts the input information its program provides; how it passes the information around; how it performs the tasks of recognition, computation, storage, and control; how it presents the end results. Fig. 41 diagrams the six basic units of a computer system. In this figure, solid-line arrows show the pathways of the *subject-matter information* (initial data, intermediate results, and answers). The dashed-line arrows show the pathways of *control information* (the "internal" instructions causing the computer units to follow the program).

Chapter 3 gave a general idea of how a computer handles information. The *control unit* is the "master-

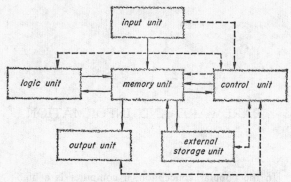

FIG. 41. Basic units of a computer system. The solid arrows show the flow of the subject matter of the computation (data and instructions); the dash-line arrows show the passage of control information from and to the control unit.

mind" of the system. It recognizes the *external* instructions provided by the program and generates *internal* instructions which direct the other units to perform their respective duties. The *memory unit* is the central repository of data and instructions; it stores and retrieves them as directed. The *logic unit* transforms the data, performing the functions of logic and arithmetic. The *input unit* brings information to the computer, data and instructions *from* the outside world (the "environment" of the computer). The *output unit* presents information *to* the environment. It permits the operator to monitor the work of the computer, and it prints out (or punches out) the answers.

In many problems, the computer must "look up" information not explicitly stated in the program, as a human computer looks up values in mathematical tables or finds unfamiliar words in a dictionary. Such information is provided to the computer by the *external storage unit*. This unit may also store information arising during the computation, particularly if the information is too voluminous or complicated to be stored in the memory unit. The external storage unit usually has a capacity far greater than the memory unit; in fact, if rolls of tape or stacks of punched cards are added as needed, its capacity may be extended indefinitely.

The sequence of operations in a typical computation involves the following major steps: The input equipment holds the program in the form of punched cards or tape. When the start button is pressed, the control unit directs the input unit to "read" the cards or tape and to transfer the program data and instructions to the memory unit, which stores them at the locations specified in the program. The input unit signals the control unit when the last item of the program has been read.

The control unit then reads the first instruction and directs the other units to follow it. This operation involves, typically, the transfer of data from the memory unit to the registers (collections of flip-flops for temporary storage) of the logic unit, followed by a command to the logic unit to perform the instructed operation on the data, followed by a further command to transfer the result to storage, either in the memory unit or in another register. This sequence of commands may be stated explicitly in the program of instruction, or it may be a "standard" sequence of operations (like those involved in the command to "add") which is called into play by a particular word in an instruction.

When the first instruction has been followed to completion, a program counter records that one instruction has been followed, and the control unit then returns to the memory unit to read the second instruction, which is followed and counted—and so on until the last instruction has been acted upon.

At any stage in this process, the control unit may call on the output unit to reveal to the operator what is going on. This happens whenever an answer, intermediate or final, is stored and the instruction calls for it to be printed out. Equally important, whenever the control unit detects a mistake (such as an incorrect parity bit, improper instruction, inconsistency in logic, lack of space in a register or the memory unit), the control unit interrupts the computation and directs the output unit to notify the operator that something is wrong. Common mistakes may be identified explicitly by the output printer or by labels on signal lights.

If the operator suspects that data have been stored incorrectly in certain memory locations, he can direct (by pressing buttons or typing an auxiliary instruction on the console typewriter) that the contents of those locations be printed out. He may even ask that the whole stored program (or a large section of it) be printed out to let him compare each stored entry with the corresponding entry in his program notebook. When the errors have been located (and corrected by typing in the correct data, instruction, memory locations, etc.), the operator then directs the control unit to resume the computation from the point where the mistake was detected.

It is a bitter fact in the life of computer operators and programmers that many hours must be consumed in finding and correcting such errors. This chore is called "debugging." It may take far more computer time than the computation itself. To reduce the time and tedium of debugging a program, techniques have been developed that use the computer itself to search for and reveal the location and nature of errors. This procedure is called "machine-aided programming." As described in the next chapter, this technique is a very powerful tool useful not only for correcting errors, but also for assembling or compiling a program in the first place.

Pulses and Bits

Information, in mechanical, electrical, or magnetic form, is the basic commodity of computer operations. One computer unit reads information, another presents it. One recognizes the meaning of information; another manipulates and translates it. All the units transfer information, as the arrows in Fig. 41 show.

Information is transferred among the units of a computer by the passage of electric current. The current flows in brief spurts, called *pulses,* which last only a few billionths of a second. The *presence* of such a pulse at a particular time represents the bit 1; the *absence* of a pulse at that time represents the bit 0.

Each character of computer language is represented by a collection ("string") of present-pulses (1's) and absent-pulses (0's) arranged according to the code representing the character. The location of each bit in the string is called a *pulse site;* that is, a place where either a present-pulse or an absent-

135

pulse is to be found. Fig. 42 shows the pulse sites for the mnemonic character 11110011 ($= C$ in Model 1401 language). The solid-line pulses are 1's, the dashed-line (absent) pulses 0's.

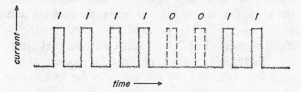

Fig. 42. Pulse chain representing the digits 11110011 in the time sequence.

The bits representing characters may be transferred one after the other ("sequentially") or together as a group ("in parallel"). A single circuit can carry the pulses in sequence, whereas a separate circuit must be provided for each bit if they are to be transferred in parallel. Evidently, the transfer is faster if the bits are handled in parallel, but correspondingly more circuits are needed. The choice between sequential and parallel transfer is thus a choice between speed and complexity, decided by the designer to achieve an economic balance between the cost and the capacity of the computer.

A given operation in the computer program must not start until the preceding one has been completed. In a *synchronous* computer a high-speed electric clock counts time intervals of the order of a few millionths of a second each, and an operation cannot start until the intervals necessary for the preceding operation have been counted out. In an

136

asynchronous computer no clock is used; instead each computer unit generates a "go-ahead" signal when it has completed its operation. This signal permits the next operation to begin. The choice between the two methods, again, is a matter of balance between complexity and speed. The synchronous computer may waste time in waiting for an interval to be completed, whereas the asynchronous computer adjusts to the time actually needed for each operation.

Input Information

The transfer of information from man to computer, in the great majority of cases, starts with a keyboard.* Direct communication with the computer is provided through the keyboard of a teletypewriter ("console keyboard") which translates the character of each key into a corresponding string of present and absent pulses. As the keys are struck in succession, pulse string follows pulse string, and these enter the other units of the computer as the contents of the typing may direct. The entire job of feeding the input information to the computer *could* be handled through this typewriter, but this never happens because manual typing is too slow. Even at the fast clip of 50 typed words per minute, the console typewriter can generate strings of pulses only at about 50 bits per second, whereas the other units of a high-speed computer are designed to handle sev-

* In this respect computers have adopted the methods of the printed word. Keyboards are used to set the type of books, magazines, newspapers, reports, and correspondence. The amount of information so handled is vast.

eral million bits per second. The console typewriter
is used only when necessary, to interrupt the program, to monitor the computation, to seek and correct errors, and in general to handle unforeseen con-
tingencies as they arise.

Input information known in advance (e.g., the
data and instructions of the program, and any other
data to be picked up from external storage) is transferred first to an intermediate storage medium, from
which it can be transferred to the computer at higher
speed. This process not only saves costly computer
time, but also provides a permanent record of the
input information.

The intermediate storage medium most used is
the punched card (Fig. 43). The card shown has

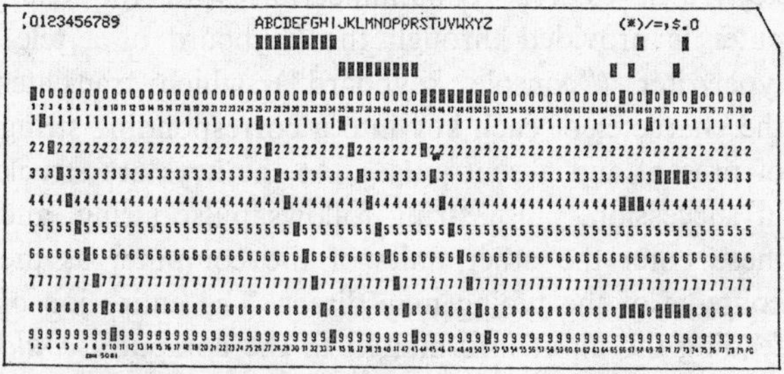

FIG. 43. Typical punched card using the Hol-
lerith code. Each symbol at the top is represented
by the holes punched directly beneath it.

960 locations ("sites") where rectangular holes may
be punched, arranged in 80 vertical columns of 12
locations each. One or more holes in a column represent a character. One hole represents each decimal digit, two holes the letters, and 1, 2, or 3 holes

138

each the signs. The pattern of holes for each character is, of course, different. As many as eighty characters can be accommodated in the width of a card, using this code. Other codes permit information to be packed more densely on the card.

The holes are made in a machine known as a *keypunch*. As each key on the board of the machine is struck, the card is punched at the locations corresponding to the code for the character on that key. The card then is moved over to the next column. When all eighty columns have been punched, the card is removed automatically and stacked. A blank card takes its place and the operation continues until the information at hand has been punched on cards.

Another storage medium is paper tape, originally devised for telegraph messages. A typical paper tape has sites for seven holes, arranged in columns across the tape. Round holes, produced by a tape keypunch, occupy these sites in patterns individually representing characters on the keyboard. As each key is struck, the holes for that character are punched and the tape advanced to the next column.

The punched card and paper tape are inexpensive, but they can accommodate only a limited number of hole sites per square inch. Information can be packed much more densely on magnetic tape, and this form of intermediate storage is used whenever a lengthy program or large store of data is to be handled. Magnetic tape for computers is similar in principle to that used in a tape recorder, but computer tape is wider and more carefully manufactured. The typical arrangement of the magnetic sites resembles that of paper tape; columns of sites are

139

arranged across the tape, perpendicular to its length. The magnetic recording head has several sections, each of which can magnetize a site in one direction (for 1's) or the other (for 0's).

A great advantage of magnetic tape, aside from its high capacity, is the fact that it can be erased (by removing the magnetism with an "erase head"). Errors can thus be corrected, old information updated, or the whole tape can be erased for reuse after it has served in a particular computation.

A single 20-inch roll of high-density magnetic tape can store as many as 100 million bits. To find a particular character or word in such an array, in a reasonable time, requires that the tape move very swiftly, and that it be stopped precisely and rapidly, without injury to the tape itself. The tape handling unit that performs these functions is a monument to the ingenuity of the mechanical and electrical engineers who have cooperated in its design.

Magnetic tape can be magnetized with a keyboard instrument that applies the appropriate magnetizing current to the sections of the recording head, in the proper direction for each 1 or 0 at each site. More often, however, punched cards are produced initially, and these are transferred to the tape in a separate operation. The information record, written on cards or tape at the slow speed of manual typing, then is transferred at higher speed to the computer proper. Information on punched cards is transferred by a device known as a *card reader*. The cards are dealt off the bottom of the stack and positioned so that the pattern of holes in each column can be determined. The presence of a hole may be detected with a metal finger. Unpunched card prevents the finger from making contact with a metal plate beneath the card. When a hole is present, the finger makes electrical contact with the plate and current flows. Twelve fingers are provided for each column, one for each hole site. Depending on which particular fingers encounter holes, currents flow in one or more of the 12 circuits connected to the fingers. These currents represent the characters. The card may be read sequentially, column by column, with only twelve fingers, or it may be read all at once, by 960 fingers. Card reading is faster than manual typing, but still very slow by computer standards. Parallel reading of the whole card is preferred when a large amount of input information is to be handled. Column-by-column reading suffices when the time consumed in input operations is not critical.

Cards may also be read with beams of light, which shine on the hole sites. Where a hole is present, the light passes to a photoelectric tube which generates a current. This operation saves wear and tear on the holes themselves and is very fast. Using parallel light-beam sensing, card readers can read as many as 2000 cards per minute, a maximum of nearly 20,000 bits per second. Paper tape can be read in a similar manner with fingers or light beams, either column by column or in parallel over a block of several adjacent columns.

Magnetic tape is read with a "reading head." This device is similar to the recording head. It is divided into sections, one for each of the magnetizable sites in each column. When a magnetized site passes a section of the head, it induces a current in one direction if the site is magnetized in the 1-direction, in the opposite direction if the magnetization is in the

0-direction. Since the sites are packed very densely, it is practical to read them only one column at a time, but all the sites in a column are (usually) read at once.

Encoding and Decoding

The currents produced with card or tape readers are usually not suitable for the computer proper but must be translated into the bit code that the computer units can recognize and manipulate. The process of translating the keyboard symbols or hole patterns into the computer code is known as *encoding*.

Consider the digits on the numeral keys on the console typewriter. Suppose we wish to translate these decimal digits into their binary equivalents. The table of the equivalents is:

Decimal	Binary
0	0000
1	0001
2	0010
3	0011
4	0100
5	0101
6	0110
7	0111
8	1000
9	1001

Ten input wires crossed by four output wires (Fig. 44-A) can represent this table. The input wires are connected to the numeral keys, 0 through 9. The four output wires represent the four bits of the binary equivalents. We place arrows to show at which

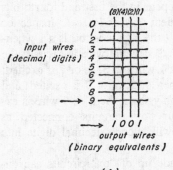

(A)

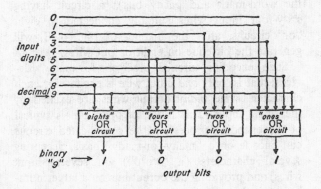

(B)

FIG. 44. Encoding circuits. (A) represents the general scheme for encoding decimal digits into their binary equivalents. (B) is a specific circuit using four "or" circuits. The arrows show the encoding of decimal 9 to binary 1001.

intersections 1-bits occur. Thus if the 9 input wire is excited, 1's must appear in the first and fourth bits of the binary equivalent ($9_{10} = 1001_2$). Inspection of the table shows that the rightmost bit is a 1 whenever the 1, 3, 5, 7, or 9 decimal wire is excited; the next bit to the left is a 1 when 2, 3, 6, or 7 is excited; the next bit is a 1 when 4, 5, 6, or 7 is excited; and the leftmost bit is 1 only when the 8 or 9 wire is excited. Therefore, four "or" circuits connected as shown in Fig. 44-B will encode decimal digits into binary ones.

Similar circuits made up of "or" circuits can encode any natural-language character into bits. The sixty-four characters and signs in Model 1401 language (Chapter 4) have eight bits each (including the word-mark and parity bits); a circuit having sixty-four input wires suitably connected to eight "or" circuits, after the manner of Fig. 44-B, will generate the bit code on eight output wires.

Such encoding circuits are "one-for-many" devices; that is, only *one* input wire is excited for each character, while *many* output wires are excited by the single input. This mode of operation is typical of the encoding process. More complicated circuits can encode on a "many-for-many" basis, accepting several characters (a "word") on several input wires, and providing the output bits on a larger number of output wires.

The opposite process of translating from bit-code to characters is known as *decoding,* a "many-for-one" process. Several input wires accept the bits representing a character, and a single output wire indicates the presence of the corresponding character. In decoding from binary numbers to their deci-

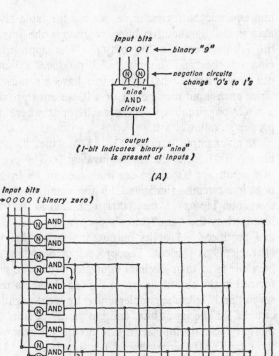

FIG. 45. Decoding circuits. (A) the elementary "and" decoder. (B) a specific circuit using 17 "and" circuits and 8 "not" circuits. The arrows show the path for decoding binary 0000 into decimal 0.

mal equivalents, for example, we use the table given above; the righthand column represents the inputs, the lefthand column the outputs. The appropriate circuit is the "and" circuit, which produces a 1-output only when *all* its input wires have 1's present. Since each input may be a 1 or a 0, we must provide a negation circuit to follow each input where the proper stimulus is a 0.

As an example, consider Fig. 45-A, which decodes binary 1001 to its decimal equivalent 9. The center two inputs are 0's; these are translated to 1's by the negation circuits (indicated by the small circles at the center inputs). When 1001 is applied to the four input wires the "and" circuit proper receives 1111 and produces a 1 at its output, indicating that the character 9 is present. The process of decoding binary digits to their decimal equivalents may be performed in the circuit shown in Fig. 45-B, which uses seven "and" circuits, supplemented by eight negation circuits for the input bits, and ten "and" circuits for the ten decimal outputs. In this circuit, for example, the input 0000 (binary "zero") is translated to 1111 by the negation circuits at the inputs of the "and" circuits shown; these bits are fed to the "0" output "and" circuit, which responds at its output with a 1, indicating the presence of decimal 0. More complicated arrangements of "and" circuits can decode several characters (a "word") at once; these have as many input wires as there are bits in the word, and one output wire for each word.

Recognition and Control

Combinations of encoder and decoder circuits can perform the basic computer functions of *recognition*

146

of external instructions by the control unit, and the *generation* of internal instructions for the other units. Suppose that the first word in an instruction is a mnemonic abbreviation for one of the arithmetical operations, ADD, SUB, MUL, or DIV. The instruction, previously encoded and stored in the memory unit as a sequence of bits, is transferred to a register in the control unit, which holds the bits in individual flip-flops. The condition (0 or 1) of each flip-flop is revealed by individual connections to the input wires of a decoder, which has been designed to react to the bit-codes for ADD, SUB, MUL, and DIV. The decoder has four output wires, one for each of these words. Thus, if the register holds the bits for ADD the ADD output wire produces a 1-bit. The presence of this bit indicates the recognition of the instruction to add. The presence of 0's on the other three output wires indicates that the other three arithmetic operations are *not* called for.

The output from the decoder is passed then to an encoder which produces, in its output wires, bits representing the internal instructions to the other computer units. These output wires, in our example, are connected to the adder circuits in the logic unit. One of the output bits permits the transfer of numbers from the memory unit of the accumulator register; another releases the adder circuits to generate the sum and carry bits, and a fourth connects (through gates) the adder output (the sum) to the accumulator register. Other output bits from the encoder prevent (by opening gates) other parts of the computer from being active during the addition operation.

Suppose the next instruction contains the bits for MUL. The instruction decoder then generates a 1-bit at its MUL output wire, and this bit goes to an encoder which translates it into a set of internal-instruction bits. These, transferred to the logic unit, set in motion the sequence of add-shift-add-shift operations which constitutes the process of multiplication (Chapter 2).

The control unit contains as many such decoder outputs as are necessary to recognize all the standard external instruction words, and these are associated with internal instruction encoders which produce the bit signals directing the other units. The decoder-encoder process is applied not only for translating external instructions into internal ones but may be used also by any computer unit to recognize internal instructions and to generate still other internal instructions (such as go-ahead signals) for another unit. There are encoding and decoding circuits by the hundreds throughout the computer. In fact, in a typical computer about half of the diodes and transistors are applied to recognition and control. The other half handles the subject matter, in registers, logic circuits, and in reading and writing on memory cores.

The encoding and decoding circuits just described are permanently wired into the computer for the standard instructions words and common operations. It also is possible to "produce" an encoding or decoding circuit to order, during a computation, by connecting individual "and," "or," and "not" circuits by gates which operate under the control of internal instructions.

Separating Data from Instructions

At this point we can grasp one of the most important facts about computers. In machine bit code the *form* of the problem (the instructions) and the *content* of the problem (the data) have exactly the same mode of expression. They are both strings of zeroes and ones. The computer can distinguish between instructions and data only if it is given some clue, such as the order in which the words are presented, or special characters such as word marks, or mnemonics which "label" the following digits. Without such clues, the computer cannot know the difference and, in point of fact, "couldn't care less."

To keep things straight, each computer instruction is written in a standard format. The first part is a mnemonic abbreviation specifying the operation to be performed. The second part contains the memory address (or addresses) where the data to be operated on are to be found, or where they are to be placed. In Chapter 3 we used instructions having three addresses (see pages 51–53).

Computers also are designed (more commonly) for single-address instructions. Typical examples are:

XMA 100   Transfer (X) the data in memory (M) location 100 to the accumulator register (A).

XAM 101   Transfer the data in the accumulator register to memory location 101.

SRA   Shift (S) one place to the right (R) the data in the accumulator register (A).

SLA   Shift one place to the left the data in the accumulator register.

CMP 102   Compare (CMP) the data in the accumulator with the data at memory location 102.

JOP 103   If the result of the previous comparison is plus, transfer the data from its previous memory location to memory location 103. (JOP is the abbreviation for "Jump on plus.")

JOM 104   If the result of the previous comparison is minus, transfer the data to memory location 104. ("Jump on minus.")

JOE 105   If the result of the previous comparison is equal (E), transfer the data to memory location 105. ("Jump on equal.")

ADD 106   Add the contents of the accumulator register to the data at memory location 106 and store the sum in the accumulator register after removing its previous contents.

MUL 107   Multiply the contents of the multiplicand register by the number stored at memory location 107, add the product to the contents of the accumulator register, place the result in the multiplicand register after removing its previous contents.

DIV 108   Divide the contents of the accumulator register by the number stored at location 108. Place the quotient in the quotient register and the remainder in the accumulator register.

In such single-address instructions operations are referred to particular registers. The accumulator register must contain the augend before the addition command is given; the sum replaces the augend in the same register. The accumulator register contains

150

the minuend before subtraction; the difference replaces the minuend in this register. Numbers in this register may be shifted left or right, one place at a time, the place vacated receiving a zero. The multiplicand must be placed in the multiplicand register before the multiplication command is given; the product is placed in the same register (the accumulator register accepts the high-order digits if the product is too long to be contained in the multiplicand register). The accumulator register must contain the dividend before the division command is given; the quotient is placed in the quotient register, and the remainder in the accumulator register.

Programmers and operators memorize very quickly the functions of these registers and thereafter can keep track of the passage of data without conscious effort. In fact, after a little practice, a programmer does not have to think about the details of data transfer at all. He uses a diagram with boxes and arrows that show the flow of information (as we shall see in the next chapter), and he writes groups of instructions, associated with the boxes and arrows, without having to visualize what the computer does with the numbers. Of course, a programmer must know how his computer handles information, particularly in finding and correcting errors, but he refers to the details only as the need arises.

This is the general outline of input operations and will suffice, I hope, to show how instructions are recognized and generated, how data are retrieved, operated upon, and stored, program-step by program-step, until the result called for is obtained. Then the data, ready for the waiting world, are transferred to the output unit.

Output Information

When ready for presentation by the output unit, the strings of pulses representing the output information are decoded, and the output wires of the decoder cause the corresponding characters to be printed for the edification of the operator or programmer or imposed on cards or tape for storage and later use, perhaps as inputs for another computation. The output can be produced by an automatic keyboard (typewriter or keypunch), whose keys are actuated by the decoder output wires. Thus the decoder of Fig. 45-B provides output signals for each of the decimal digits, and these signals cause the numeral keys to strike. Other decoder outputs actuate the letter and sign keys.

Such automatic keyboards can operate faster than a typist can manipulate the keys manually, but they are very slow by computer standards because the characters must be printed or punched one after another. The keyboard output is limited to about ten characters per second, whereas a computer can provide decoded output at rates better than 100,000 characters per second. To avoid costly waste of computer time (the larger computers rent for more than $10 per minute!) it has been necessary to devise output printers that can print many characters at once.

A typical high-speed printer can print fifteen lines of type, each containing 120 characters, each second, literally spewing out paper. One form of high-speed printer employs 120 character wheels (one wheel for each character location in the line of typing) which rotate on a shaft. Each wheel contains all the characters (letters, numbers, signs) embossed on its periphery. Opposite each wheel is a hammer which presses the paper (and interposed typewriter ribbon) against the wheel at the proper instant to cause the desired character to be printed on the paper.

The character wheels are aligned on the shaft so that a given character (say "E") is presented by each wheel at the same time. When the character E is in position, those hammers strike at every position in the line where an E is to be printed; that is, all the E's on that line are printed at once. When the wheels have rotated to the next character other hammers strike at the positions where that character is to be printed on the same line, and so on, until the wheels have completed one rotation and the whole line has been printed. Then the paper is advanced to the next line, and the process repeats.

For this operation the characters provided by the computer output for a line of typing must be stored while the line is being typed (that is, for one revolution of the character wheels). During that time, signals representing like characters are drawn from storage for each position of the wheels, and these signals cause the hammers to strike at the proper positions along each line. The circuits associated with a high-speed printer must store all the characters for a line and select them character by character, keeping track of their intended positions in the line. The memory and logic circuits required are, of course, no different in principle from those used in the other units of the computer.

Those electrically and mechanically minded readers who wish to pursue the details of computer hardware can find books† on this fascinating but highly complex subject. Others must accept on faith the computer designers' ability to hook up the basic circuits for logic, storage, recognition, and control as building blocks, to interconnect them with wires, gates, switches, in order to produce a machine incorporating tens of thousands of diodes, transistors, and hundreds of thousands of cores—and keep their sanity while doing it. If your faith is of this order you are ready to investigate the other half of computer science, the writing of programs.

† For example, *Computer Logic: The Functional Design of Digital Computers,* by Ivan Flores (Prentice-Hall, 1960).

CHAPTER 8

PROGRAMS AND SOFTWARE

> For precept must be upon precept, precept upon
> precept; line upon line, line upon line; here a little
> and there a little; . . . Now go, write it before
> them in a table, and note it in a book . . .
> —THE BIBLE, ISAIAH *28*, 13; *30*, 8

At this stage it is quite evident that solving problems
with a computer requires an intricate partnership
between man and machine. The computer does what
man directs it to do; man exerts his control with
programs written in some form of computer language. In this chapter we seek a closer acquaintance
with computer programs—how they are planned,
written, and translated from natural language to machine code. We shall return to our computation of
π, and show how a professional programmed this
problem for an actual computer (G.E. Model 225).
Then, we shall see how the computer itself may be
used to assist the programmer in assembling and
compiling the detailed steps of the program.

The steps followed in writing a computer program
fall into four main categories: First, the programmer
defines the problem; that is, he restates it in terms

appropriate for machine computation. Second, he draws a *systems flow chart* embodying the equipment used in the problem-solving routine. Third, he draws another chart, the *logic flow chart,* that shows in detail the steps the computer must be instructed to take to reach the answers. Fourth, with the logic chart as a guide, he writes a table of instructions, using the mnemonic abbreviations which his computer is designed to decode. He may do this by hand (manual coding) or he may use the machine to help him (machine-assisted coding). The result is line upon line of instructions which, little by little, carry the computer through the program. The experienced programmer also follows Isaiah's injunction and "notes it in a book," recording for future reference the steps in his reasoning.

Defining the π Problem

We have defined the π problem, for human calculators, in Chapter 4 (pages 63 to 65). For a computer, we must define each term in the π series in precise and general form. We must find, in other words, a mathematical expression for each term. In the series we have used, each term, you will recall, has the numerator 4, the denominators are the odd integers, and the signs of the terms alternate between plus and minus. If we let N be the number of the term ($N = 1$ for the first term, $N = 2$ for the second, and so on), we find that the *magnitude* of the "Nth" term is:

$$\text{Magnitude of Term } N = \frac{4}{(2N-1)}$$

We can check this formula by substituting $N = 1, 2,$ 3, etc., and comparing the values with the magnitudes of the corresponding terms in the series (Chapter 1, page 10).

The *sign* of the Nth term can be expressed as a power of -1:

$$\text{Sign of Term } N = (-1)^{N+1}$$

as we can confirm by substituting 1, 2, 3, etc., for N. The *signed value* of the Nth term is then:

$$N\text{th term} = (-1)^{N+1} \cdot \frac{4}{(2N-1)}$$

The routine for computing 100 terms is now fairly obvious. We instruct the computer first to compute the magnitude using $N = 1$, then to compute the sign for $N = 1$, and to multiply the results. This operation produces the signed magnitude of the first term, which is stored at the first of the memory locations reserved for the terms (locations 0101 to 0200 in our problem). Then the machine changes N from 1 to 2 and repeats the process, forming the second term and storing it in the second location reserved for the terms. The process repeats until $N = 100$, and 100 terms have been computed and stored.

The next step is to add the terms stored in the first 98 memory locations, producing the "98-term sum," and to store it at a specified location (1098 in our problem). Then the 99th term is added to the result, producing the "99-term sum," which is stored at 1099. Finally the 100th term is added to the latter result, producing the "100-term sum," which is stored at 1100.

The next instruction asks the computer to examine the values of the 98-, 99-, and 100-term sums, which must be less, greater, and less respectively than the given value of π. If these values are correct the program proceeds to the next step. Otherwise, the computer is instructed to print "Error in Magnitude of Sum." The programmer then examines the output and his logic chart to determine what is wrong.

The next instruction calls for the computation of the *average* of the 98-term and 99-term sums, which is stored (at location 1108 in our problem). Then the average of the 99-term and 100-term sums is produced and stored at location 1109. The average of the two averages is computed and stored at location 1110. This last result is compared with the given approximate value of $\pi = 3.141592$ (which has previously been stored at location 1111). The program instructs the computer to print "problem solved" if there is agreement in every digit. Otherwise, "problem unsolved" is printed. The final instruction is a notification to the computer that the exercise is finished. The machine stops, holding all the data in its memory until it is cleared for the next problem.

In our simple example we have defined the program in words in four paragraphs. But most computer exercises are not so simple, and it is usual for the programmer to plot out the program plan graphically, in the logic flow chart previously mentioned. The logic flow chart for the π problem is shown in Fig. 46. If we compare the boxes and arrows with the program outline of the preceding paragraphs, we find that they contain the same information. The chart, however, is much easier to follow. It permits

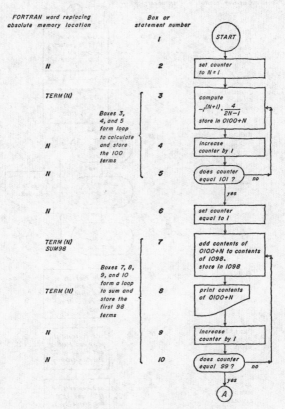

FORTRAN word replacing absolute memory location	Box or statement number	
	1	START
N	*2*	set counter to N = 1
TERM (N)	*3*	compute $-1^{(N+1)} \cdot \frac{4}{2N-1}$ store in O100+N
N	*4*	increase counter by 1
N	*5*	does counter equal 101 ? no
N	*6*	set counter equal to 1
TERM (N) SUM98	*7*	add contents of O100+N to contents of I098. store in I098
TERM (N)	*8*	print contents of O100+N
N	*9*	increase counter by 1
N	*10*	does counter equal 99 ? no
		A

Boxes 3, 4, and 5 form loop to calculate and store the 100 terms

Boxes 7, 8, 9, and 10 form a loop to sum and store the first 98 terms

FIG. 46. Systems flow chart for computing and checking π to six decimal places.

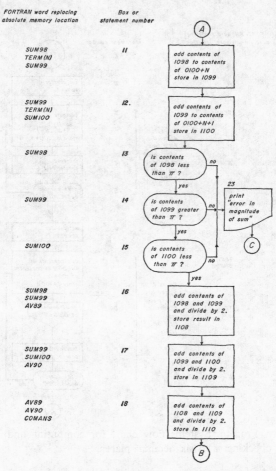

FORTRAN word replacing absolute memory location	Box or statement number	
SUM98 TERM(N) SUM99	11	add contents of 1098 to contents of 0100+N store in 1099
SUM99 TERM(N) SUM100	12.	add contents of 1099 to contents of 0100+N+1 store in 1100
SUM98	13	is contents of 1098 less than π ?
SUM99	14	is contents of 1099 greater than π ?
SUM100	15	is contents of 1100 less than π ?
	23	print "error in magnitude of sum"
SUM98 SUM99 AV89	16	add contents of 1098 and 1099 and divide by 2. store result in 1108
SUM99 SUM100 AV90	17	add contents of 1099 and 1100 and divide by 2. store in 1109
AV89 AV90 COMANS	18	add contents of 1108 and 1109 and divide by 2. store in 1110

FIG. 46—Continued

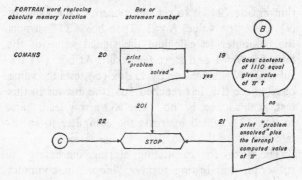

Fig. 46—*Continued*

us to see the plan at a glance, and to understand the sequence of the instructions from start to finish of the program. Note that rectangular boxes are used to enclose instructions which do not involve comparisons. When a comparison is required the box has rounded ends, with one arrow leading into it, and two or more arrows leading out. The emerging arrows are labeled with the results of the comparison ("yes" or "no"; "equal" or "not equal").

Logic Flow Chart of the π Program

Having laid out the program in general terms, we next must examine in detail the logic chart (Fig. 46), which indicates the individual steps and paths of logic that the computer must follow. Follow this figure carefully, because it illustrates important processes not yet considered. At the top of Fig. 46-A, you will find the start of the program, a round box numbered (1). The next step, given by the instruction in box (2), is to set the subscript (the value of N) to its first value, $N = 1$. Then box (3) instructs the computer to calculate the signed value of the term for $N = 1$ and store the result. At box (4) the subscript N is increased by 1. Box (5) tests the value of N to see if it has reached 101; the answer to this test, at this stage, is "no." The NO arrow leads back to box (3), which instructs the computer to calculate and store the next value of the term.

The boxes for calculating, storing, increasing the subscript, and testing form a "loop." In computer terminology, a "loop" comprises instructions that are to be used many times over. This device eliminates the writing of the instructions every time they are needed. The "loop" of boxes (3, 4, and 5) calculates, stores, increases the subscript, and tests its value. The loop terminates the term computation when 100 different values of the term have been calculated and stored.

The first term is stored in memory location $0100 + N$ or 0101. The second term is stored in location 0102, and so on to location 0200 for term 100. When the 100th term is calculated and stored, the value of N becomes 101 and the answer to box (5) becomes "yes," opening the loop, and the YES arrow transfers the logic path to box (6) where the value of N is reset to 1, in preparation for summing the terms.

The summation of terms is illustrated by box (7). The first term, the contents of $0100 + N$ (= 0101 since $N = 1$), is added to the contents of location 1098 (initially zero) and the result is stored in the same location (1098). Note that this location can be used for both addition and storing because these operations take place in succession; that is, the contents of 1098 are not destroyed until the next addition of the term is stored in that location.

Box (8) instructs the computer to print the current value of the term. This statement can be deleted from the program (as we show later) since printing the values of the terms is not an essential part of the problem as we have defined it. The statement can be used in debugging the program or to preserve the actual value of each of the terms.

Box (9) increases the value of N by 1 (N now equals 2). Box (10) tests the value of N against the value 99. Since N has not yet reached this value the NO arrow leads back to box (7), which produces the sum of the second term and the first.

Boxes (7), (8), (9), and (10) form a loop for summing the first 98 terms. For the first 98 times around the loop the answer to the test will be "no." After the 98th term has been summed, however, the value of N becomes 99 and the answer to the test is "yes." The YES arrow leads to box (11) where the 99th term (since N is now 99) is added to the 98-term sum (location 1098) and the result is stored in location 1099. Next, box (12) retrieves the 100th term, since N is still 99 and the location is $(0100 + N + 1) = 0200$ and adds the 99-term sum from location 1099. The result is stored in location 1100. At this stage, the computer has computed 100 terms, stored at locations 0101 through 0200, and three sums stored at 1098, 1099, and 1100.

Next, following our "human program" of Chapter 4, we test the 98th, 99th, and 100th term sums for their magnitudes relative to 3.141592. These tests are performed in order by decision boxes (13), (14), and (15). NO arrows of these boxes cause the message ERROR IN MAGNITUDE OF SUM to be printed. The YES arrows lead to the next box and finally (the relative values all having been found correct) to the next instruction. This box (16) computes the average of the 98- and 99-term sums, and places the result in location 1108. The next box (17) finds the average of the 99- and 100-term sums, and places the result in location 1109. Box (18) takes the average of the two averages and places the result in location 1110.

The decision box (19) then asks whether the final average is equal to the given value of π (3.141592). If the answer is equal, the printer is instructed, by box (20), to print PROBLEM SOLVED; if not, the printer is instructed by box (21) to print PROBLEM UNSOLVED. The final instruction, following either message, is "stop the computer," box (22).

Having gone through this diagram in detail, we should remember two important items. The first is the use of the subscript N to shift from one term to the next. This operation permits a single computation (with N embodied in it) to be used over and over again, forming a new result for each value of N. The second is the use of a decision box to terminate the loop when the specified value of N has been reached.

Having examined the detailed logic chart, we now proceed to the fourth step—writing the instructions in the code which the computer can understand (that is, using language which the computer has been designed to decode). Many of the boxes in

Fig. 46 require several machine-language instructions. For example, box (3) requires instructions for forming $2N$, subtracting 1 from $2N$, storing $2N - 1$, placing the number 4 in a register, retrieving $2N - 1$ and dividing this into the contents of the register, placing the quotient in a memory location for later retrieval as a multiplicand. Box (3) also calculates $N + 1$ by placing N in the register and adding one to it. The result is stored temporarily. A minus one is then placed in the register and multiplied by itself $N + 1$ times. The product appears in the register, and this is multiplied by the multiplicand previously stored. Since this coding must be performed 100 times (one for each term), it would be very tedious to rewrite the instructions. Rather, one set of instructions for the computation of box (3) is written and stored in memory as machine language. The instructions are retrieved (with the proper value of N) each time they are needed.

The programmer himself might do all this work, using machine language, but for many reasons he shies away. First, if he makes even a slight error in the early stages of writing the instructions (such as writing 0110 for a memory location, when he meant 0101) all the subsequent steps of the program may be in error, and he has to do it over. The next time around he may make another error, and so it may go until his incipient ulcers become chronic. Even if long practice makes the programmer reasonably error-free, the tedium of the job acts as inspiration to find a better way. The better way is machine-aided coding (using programs called "assemblers" or "compilers"), in which all the details of assigning memory locations, setting up loops, computing terms and adding them, devising routines for dividing, averaging, storing and retrieving, etc., are left to the computer itself. In Chapter 4 we reported that programming aids known as "software" may be used to write a program in plain English (or at least in a stylized and abbreviated form of English). This procedure leaves all the details of the coding to the computer. Since the machine has superhuman accuracy, it almost never makes errors on its own account.

There are many forms of machine-aided coding. They go by such esoteric names as relative addressing, symbolic addressing, interpretive coding, assembling, and compiling. It is beyond our scope to examine these in detail. Rather, we shall take a specific case, the compiler language known as FORTRAN (from *for*mula *tran*slation). This programming aid is widely used to write engineering and scientific programs and it is appropriate for our π problem. Other compiler languages, notably COBOL (*co*mmon *b*usiness-*o*riented *l*anguage) have been developed to aid in writing programs for business applications. (The U. S. Government has served notice that it will not buy or rent any computer unless it has been adapted to use COBOL.) Today, nearly every general purpose computer is set up for COBOL and FORTRAN compilation, and there are many variations of these for special purposes. (The U. S. Military Academy at West Point instructs its cadets with a version of FORTRAN known as CADETRAN.)

The FORTRAN Program for π

Perhaps the best way to introduce FORTRAN is the following narrative of what happened when we put our π problem on the G.E. Model 225 computer at West Point. The programmer* previously had spent about an hour drawing the logic flow chart (Fig. 46). With this chart at hand, he wrote out thirty-one statements on a coding sheet, each a stylized instruction in FORTRAN. These statements are spelled out, with explanations, in the appendix of this book. The writing consumed about fifteen minutes. The programmer then keypunched thirty-one cards, one for each of the FORTRAN statements. The punching operation took about five minutes. This deck of cards, the *source deck,* contained the problem as formulated by the programmer "at the source," that is, as it was stated in the logic chart.

Next, the programmer went to the computer library and took out a stack of punched cards about two inches thick, labeled FORTRAN Compiler. These cards, actually a complex program in themselves, had been punched previously by the manufacturer of the computer. They contained all the FORTRAN symbols and words, all the rules of syntax of the language, a list of commonly committed errors, and large amounts of other data which comprise the routines for recognizing FORTRAN statements and translating them into the Model 225 machine language. This compiler deck was the distilled result of many months of effort on the part of a team of program specialists (at Phoenix, Arizona)

---

* Mr. Jerry Foster, of the General Electric Computer Department, to whom we are greatly indebted for his help. The computer used is for instruction of West Point cadets, then under the supervision of Major H. W. Lombard, to whom we are also most grateful for his ready willingness to assist in the writing of this book.

whose project it was to adapt the Model 225 computer to accept FORTRAN instructions.

The programmer cleared the computer memory of all content and placed the compiler deck in the hopper of the card reader. On top of this deck he placed the thirty-one cards of the source deck. Then he pressed the start button. The reader chattered away, reading the cards while the computer stored all the FORTRAN routines in its memory. The computer memory was transformed from empty storehouse into a fullblown library of standard FORTRAN procedures. The computer, on reaching the source deck cards, read them, analyzed each statement, and selected from its memory the routines that would be appropriate to solve the problem. It thus produced the machine language needed for each statement. These routines it assembled and compiled in the correct order to instruct itself, in its own language, to perform the steps specified in the source deck. Then the card computer's automatic punch punched out cards (the *object deck*) which represented the compiled program in machine code.

Next the programmer took from the library another two sets of cards, labeled FORTRAN prefix and FORTRAN suffix.† Between these two sets he inserted the cards of the object deck, making one deck of cards which was to place our particular problem in the machine. This combined deck he

† The PREFIX is a "loader" which places in memory at the correct locations the object deck machine language instructions and the necessary routines of the SUFFIX. The SUFFIX is divided into the "non-optional" and "optional" routines. The former are needed in every program while the latter are loaded only if called on by the programmer through certain names and symbols.

loaded into the card reader, and again he pressed the start button. The reader again chattered, and the problem was loaded, in forty-five seconds. Now the computer memory contained the FORTRAN procedures associated with our problem as well as the contents of the object deck.

The loading completed, the computer automatically began to "execute" the computation of the value of π and to compare it with the given value. After a pause of a second or two (during which the computer was actually processing data at a rate of several million bits per second), the output printer began to whir. The instructions called for the value of each term to be printed out. Consequently, in thirty-two seconds 101 lines were printed out, 100 of which were the term values and the last of which was "problem solved." Most of this time was taken in printing the values of the individual terms. To give a better idea of how long it took the computer to compute, it is worth mentioning that the programmer, by removing the card containing FORTRAN Statement 8 (see Appendix), altered the routine to omit printing the term values. This time the computer took only three seconds to complete the job! Those readers who have taken the time to compute our problem by hand (it took your author, working alone, nearly ten hours) will begin to realize what the million-times speed advantage of the computer means in practice.

In summary, it took our expert programmer about eighty minutes to understand the problem, to draw the logic chart, write the FORTRAN statements, and punch the source deck. Then it took about 160 seconds of machine time to compile the object deck, load it, and execute the computation.

How a Compiler Works

To learn all there is to know about a compiler language like FORTRAN is a task not everyone cares to undertake, but the main ideas are not difficult. The cards in the compiler deck, punched with instructions in machine code, cause the computer to perform these principal tasks:

(1) To analyze each FORTRAN statement by recognizing the symbols (numbers, letters and words) and translating them into the corresponding machine language instructions;

(2) To place the name of each variable used by the programmer into a table for later reference;

(3) To allocate a memory location for each variable and associate it with the arithmetic instructions;

(4) To arrange the machine language instructions in the proper sequence to solve the problem (in this, the computer actually follows the logic of Fig. 46);

(5) To print out the source deck statements for inspection by programmer, as well as messages which identify any errors the programmer has made; and

(6) To punch out the machine instructions on cards (the object deck).

These are, of course, very similar to the steps that a programmer would use if he were compiling the program by hand. The fact that these tasks can be assigned to the machine is one of the great achievements in the technology of this century.

Let us examine, as an example of computer operations, the recognition and analysis of arithmetic symbols. FORTRAN uses the following symbols for arithmetic:

Symbol	Meaning
+	Add the preceding and following quantities.
—	Subtract the following quantity from the preceding quantity.
*	Multiply the preceding and following quantities.
/	Divide the preceding quantity by the following quantity.
**	Raise the preceding quantity to the power given by the following quantity.

We can illustrate the use of these symbols by the notation for the signed magnitude of the Nth term in the π series:

Ordinary Notation

$$(-1)^{(N+1)} \cdot \frac{(2N-1)}{4}$$

FORTRAN Notation‡

$$(-1**(N+1))*(4./(2.*N-1))$$

What happens when the card reader encounters

‡ The decimal points in the magnitude portion of the FORTRAN expression are important. They signify to the computer that the magnitude of the term is to be computed in "floating point" form; that is, as decimal fractions multiplied by powers of 10. The absence of decimal points in the sign portion signifies that this computation is in "fixed point" form; that is, integers only.

171

this FORTRAN notation? First, it meets the initial parenthesis. This puts the compiler on notice that a closing parenthesis must follow in this statement. As the compiler proceeds, it finds another set of intervening parentheses, which must be closed before the initial parenthesis is closed. Following this is a single asterisk. The asterisk means the entire preceding quantity is a multiplicand and the entire following quantity is its multiplier. The following portion is then read until the final closing parenthesis is found.

The compiler must now produce the coding for performing this portion of the computation. It does so by clues given by the parentheses and the order of the symbols. It works with the inner sets in parentheses, then with the outer, left to right, and devises the following detailed instructions:

Look at memory location N and put its contents in the accumulator register.§ Add 1 to the contents of the register and store the result in a memory location reserved for this addition. Place -1 in the accumulator register. Multiply this by -1 and repeat until -1 has been multiplied by itself $N+1$ times, by reference to the stored value of $N+1$. Store the result $(-1**(N+1))$ in a location that has been reserved for this multiplication. Once again place the contents of location N in the accumulator register. Convert the contents of the register into a floating point number. Multiply the contents of the accumulator register by a floating point two, and place the floating

§ The "accumulator" is a special register which holds data, such as addends or multiplicands, which are to be combined with other numbers (augends or multipliers) and which thereafter receives the result (sum or product).

point product $2N$ in the accumulator register. Subtract from the floating point number $2N$ a floating point 1 and place the difference $2N-1$ in the accumulator. Divide the contents of this location into a floating point 4. Place the floating point answer in the accumulator register. Now go back and retrieve the contents of the location where $(-1^{**}(N+1)$ is stored. Convert this number to floating point. Multiply the contents of the accumulator register—the value $(4/(2N-1)$—by $(-1^{**}(N+1)$. Store the product (in floating point). This is the computation of $(-1^{**}(N+1))^{*}(4./(2.^{*}N-1))$.

This coding serves to compute the sign and magnitude of the Nth term. A previous source statement (DIMENSION) has advised the compiler that there would be 100 answers to the computation, so the necessary memory locations were reserved. The answer to the first term is placed in the first of these reserved memory locations. Then instructions from the source statements increase the value of N by 1. Further instruction causes the computation to be performed again, forming the signed magnitude of term 2, and storing it at the second reserved memory location—and so on until all 100 locations are filled with the computations of the respective terms.

The computer's production of such coding, without aid from the programmer, is possible only because a great deal of thought has gone into the compiler program. All the usual combinations of arithmetic symbols, arrangements of parentheses, and sequences of operations have been anticipated and made a part of the logical design embodied in the compiler deck. To keep matters in hand, certain usages of characters, symbols, and sequences must be ruled out, and these restrictions result in the FORTRAN rules, which must be learned and strictly observed by the programmer who produces the source deck. But if the rules are observed the computer equipped for FORTRAN will read the statement, analyze it, and produce the machine language instructions. Moreover, it makes a list of all the programmer's names and symbols and the memory locations where they are stored. Thus the symbols and names, once established, can be used in other statements without redefinition.

Wonderful as the production of this particular set of machine instructions is, the computer must perform a more ambitious task; it must produce the *over-all* routine (the object deck) by sorting out and arranging all the instructions so that they proceed without waste effort from beginning to end of the program. Some of the most sophisticated work in computer science underlies the steady improvement of compiler language.

Compiler Addressing

A feature worth noting is the compiler's use of symbols or names (not numbers) to identify memory locations. In the beginning of this chapter, when the problem definition was given for the π problem, we used numbers for memory locations (e.g., locations 0101 through 0200 for the storage of the 100 terms). Actually, of course, the computer finds a memory location by referring to its number expressed in bits. But with compilers, programmers have to remember only symbols or names, which are much easier to remember than numbers.

Suppose we instruct the computer (as a part of the compilation process) to set aside an array of 100 positions through the FORTRAN statement of DIMENSION TERM (100). The compiler will assign 100 memory locations to the name TERM, but the programmer does not need to know, or care, which 100 memory locations are used. In this manner the programmer can use TERM or TERM(N) as the *general* location of the array and N as the *position* within the array. The position of the array is found by setting N equal to a value of 1 to 100, and the particular memory location is found by adding the value of N to the memory location associated with TERM.

This procedure is of great value in writing a program in English names and symbols. It permits the programmer to select his own word for a particular quantity. The compiler makes a record of this word and its memory location and thereafter identifies the same word with the same memory location.

The equals sign is one of the most powerful of the FORTRAN symbols. In our FORTRAN program (see Appendix, Statements 1, 2, and 3), the signed magnitude of the first term is written:

```
DIMENSION TERM(100)
N = 1
TERM(N) = (-1**(N+1))*(4./(2.*(N-1)))
```

To the programmer this means he has reserved 100 locations for the name TERM, and set the subscript to the first position of the 100 locations. TERM(N) then is the first position and the location where the computation on the right side of the equals sign will be stored. N is used on both sides of the equals sign but has different meanings. In other words, the symbols to the left of the equals sign identify memory locations of the answers; those to the right identify values to be computed.

Since the compiler is busy making lists from the programmer's names and symbols, and since the object instructions produced require more memory locations, the computer could run out of memory locations on large and complex programs before the compilation is completed. The compiler will alert the programmer with an error message when the memory becomes full. If this happens, the programmer must break the statements down into groups that can be compiled separately, the portion completed being stored on an auxiliary memory unit (such as magnetic tape) before the computer compiles the next portion. When problems of this type are being run, the current portion is executed, and the second (and third, etc.) portion is read in from the external storage device. This operation is called overlaying. Care must be used by the programmer not to impose the next portion on memory locations that must be used by all portions of the program.

The extent to which machine-aided programming has been pushed in recent years is nothing short of startling. One of the most amazing "software" items is the "report writer." This type of program causes a computer to search its magnetic tape files for requested data, to perform logical and arithmetical operations on them, to reach conclusions, and to print out a report which can be understood by someone quite ignorant of computer science.

An executive of a grocery chain, for example, may ask for a report, by forwarding the following request to his chief programmer: "Give me a list of all our retail outlets whose gross sales, in the past three months, have exceeded $100,000 and tell me the net earnings of each for that period." A few sentences in plain language, only slightly recast from the words of this request, plus a few special parameters, can be fed into the computer by the report-writer program. Without further ado, the requested list will be forthcoming automatically from the computer, the machine having searched its file of the sales records and computed the earnings as instructed.

Experiments with *spoken* computer instructions (not *typewritten*) have been under way for several years, and many computer experts expect that direct communication by microphone and loudspeaker between man and machine will be possible, and economically feasible, within the next decade or two.

The aspects of computer software that we have been able to sketch in these pages are, of course, only a beginning, but the survey of things that computers are doing every day should give us some preparation for the main question of this book: What, if it does exist, is artificial intelligence? This, needless to say, is a controversial subject that can benefit from a sifting of sense from nonsense. A reasonable approach to the question would seem to include a look at the mechanisms of human intelligence, which will occupy us in the next chapter.

CHAPTER 9

THE BRAIN AT WORK

The brain is like a computing machine, but
there is no computing machine like the brain.
—Dr. Warren McCulloch

The natural mechanisms employed in intelligent
thought and action would make a large subject, and
we must limit our attention to those aspects of natural intelligence that most directly illuminate artificial
intelligence.

The study of human intelligence is carried forward, for the most part, in two life sciences, physiology and psychology. Physiology is the study of
how our bodies are put together and how our vital
organs operate and function together. The physiologist explores the brain, so to speak, from inside the
skull. He identifies the parts of the brain, traces the
pathways of the nervous system, and measures its
electrical and chemical properties. In the language
of physics, chemistry, and biology he describes
the interplay of the organs involved in sensation,
thought, and action.

Psychology, on the other hand, is concerned primarily with behavior. How the human being as a whole responds to, and acts in, his environment is the substance of the science. The psychologist studies intelligence from outside the skull. He is interested in how we perceive the complex patterns presented to our senses, how we translate knowledge and desires into action, how we learn from experience. He views the brain, nerves, sense organs, and muscles as a *system* and he attempts to understand —and to predict—how that system will react to patterns of stimulation from the world around it. He is concerned not so much with physics and chemistry as with thought and emotion, particularly as they are expressed in conscious behavior and subconscious drives. In particular, he identifies thought with *language;* that is, the words and other symbols we use in organizing our intelligent actions.

The study of artificial intelligence similarly embraces two principal disciplines. The "physiology" of computers is the study of their parts and interconnections—tapes, transistors, magnetic cores, indicators, push buttons, and electronic circuits. The computer "physiologist" is the engineer who designs the computer to perform its functions. The computer "psychologist," on the other hand, concentrates on the functions. An expert in computation, he frames the plan of action which transforms the questions into the answers. He may be, and often is, quite ignorant of the detailed inner workings of the computer, but he is an expert in *computer language;* that is, the numbers, words, and programs which express the computation plan.

Questions and Answers

We start, then, with a brief look at the human apparatus for intelligence—the brain and the nervous system that connects it with our sense organs and muscles. Fig. 47 illustrates the pathway from

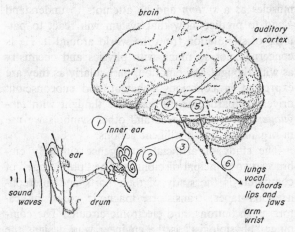

FIG. 47. Pathways of an act of human intelligence—answering a question. The numbers refer to the steps described in the text.

stimulation to response in a typical classroom situation. The teacher asks, "Who can tell the class why an astronaut in orbit feels no sense of gravity?" The class responds, depending on how well they have prepared the lesson, *either* by raising hands *or* by looking entirely disinterested. In arriving at this decision to participate or hold aloof, the pupils perform an act of intelligence involving six basic steps:

1. *Perception and Analysis.* The sound waves of the teacher's voice impinge on eardrums, which vibrate. Each eardrum moves three small bones (hammer, anvil, and stirrup) in sympathy. This mechanical motion is transmitted through the fluid of the inner ear to a group of cells ("hair cells"), which are twisted, squeezed, or bent in various ways, depending on the pitch, loudness, and timbre of the sounds of the teacher's voice. Attached to each hair cell is a fiber of the auditory nerve. Each nerve fiber is stimulated, by the motions of its associated hair cell, to generate a series of electrical impulses. The auditory nerve as a whole, composed of many thousands of fibers, thus has presented to it many separate electrical signals, each of which represents a different component of the sound wave. The teacher's question is thus *analyzed* by the ear into separate electrical messages, each carrying impressions corresponding to pitch, loudnesses, and timbre.

2. *Transmission of the Message Pattern.* The auditory nerve carries the electrical signals to the brain, and each of its fibers preserves its portion of the signal pattern substantially separate from those carried by the other fibers. The pattern, which represents the ear's analysis of the sound wave, is thus maintained during its passage to the brain. Moreover, this pattern is unique to the specific question posed by the teacher, and to the special quality of his voice. The message pattern carries not only the meaning of the question, but also many other incidental items of intelligence, whereby the class can recognize (even with eyes closed) who the teacher is and whether he is in a good mood.

The message pattern extends in space (distributed

among the thousands of nerve fibers) and in time (from the beginning to the end of the question). There are literally millions of possible space-and-time variations in the message pattern, each separately recognizable by the brain. One important variation is determined, for example, by the position of the teacher in the classroom. If he is to the right, the pupils' right ears will vibrate and analyze the sound wave a fraction of a second earlier than the left ears, and this subtle difference in timing, detected in the two halves of the brain, will provide a clue to his position in the room.

Thus far in our example we are on reasonably firm ground. Anatomists have actually traced the ear's analysis of sound and measured the electrical message pattern in the auditory nerve, but at this point the message pattern enters the brain, and here we lose track of the details. We can trace the principal nerve paths through the parts of the brain, and in the lower animals (such as the frog) we can identify many of the brain functions separately. But the human brain is so complex (there are some 13,000,-000,000 neurons in the brain and central nervous system, and each of these has, on the average, several hundred connections to other neurons) that we cannot measure its actions. We can only draw inferences from gross observations of the brain at work. From here on we describe, with little experimental confirmation, what brain experts believe to be happening. Since these beliefs are an essential part of the comparative study of natural and artificial intelligence, we proceed with the understanding that many of the concepts are the "best guesses" of the life scientists.

182

3. *Sorting at the Message Center.* The auditory nerve, like the nerves associated with the sense of smell (olfactory nerve) and sight (optic nerve), terminates at the brainstem, just above the upper end of the spinal column. This is the "message center" of the brain. Still other nerves reach the brainstem through the spinal column. These transmit impressions of pressure, pain, temperature, from the more remote parts of the body, by message patterns from some 4,000,000 sense detectors embedded in the skin.

The brainstem is flooded with simultaneous sense impressions from all parts of the body. It is estimated that in every second of our waking lives our sense organs generate at least 100,000,000 electrical impulses. Evidently we cannot respond at once to all these signals. Some are redirected (by reflex action) by the spinal cord. The remainder reach the brainstem, which sorts out the messages, suppressing many as of no special importance, passing on a few that require the special attention of the conscious mind. Each second, about 100 nerve impulses—only one in a million—reach the highest centers of conscious thought, in the cortex of the brain.

We have only the barest idea of how the brainstem acts as the message center of the brain. We do know that it does not—indeed it could not—act entirely on its own. It controls, and is controlled by, other parts of the brain, and its actions are determined not only by the incoming sense messages but by other messages which represent our past experiences. We thus encounter the mystery of human memory. Without memory, human intelligence could hardly exist. Neither could artificial intelligence. Computer systems capable of imitating the mind must have memory cells, and the closer they come to imitating the higher reaches of intelligence the more memory cells they must have.

Before the brainstem will pass on the teacher's question (in our hypothetical classroom) to the conscious mind, it must determine that the question is the main event to be dealt with, among the thousands of sense-messages it receives at the same time. It does this by many clues. Through a pressure-message each pupil knows he is sitting in his accustomed classroom seat. Through a sight-message he sees the teacher. Through a memory-message he knows he has had a lesson to study and a recitation to prepare. So, when the teacher's question is posed, the brainstem is ready for it. It sorts out the essential content of the meaning of the question and passes on, in a much simplified form, another message to the higher brain, the cortex.

This marvelous achievement, compressing a complex sense message into a much simpler summary for conscious interpretation, can be explained only if we imagine that the brainstem (aided by other parts of the brain) is using a *code* which translates and refines the raw "input data" from the ear into the refined form suitable for the processes of thought. We know, from electrical analysis, that the sound wave, in the five seconds of the teacher's question, contains at least 50,000 significant variations in air pressure which are perceived and analyzed by the ear. Yet psychological testing shows that a person perceives consciously in that time only about 250 information clues, which are acted upon in forming and speaking an answer to the question.

184

This code-translation in the brainstem is carried out, we believe, with sets of symbols, which are arranged in sequences, like the letters in sentences, to form the refined message for the cortex. No one has yet "cracked the code" that links the sense pulses to the meaning of the thought pattern. But we have every reason to believe that the code is arranged along the lines of a language, consisting of symbols (letters) which can be arranged in groups (words, phrases, and sentences) to convey meaning. In the higher process of conscious thinking the symbols of language must be present a good part of the time because we observe our own silent use of words in arriving at answers to questions.

4. *Recognizing the Content of the Question.* From the brainstem, the refined message pattern passes through two subsidiary nerve centers (which participate in the code translation process) to the portion of the brain that recognizes the meaning of sounds, the *auditory cortex.* This is located in two areas at the left and right of the outer portion of the brain. These auditory areas have been examined in great detail in the brains of laboratory animals, and during surgery on diseased or damaged human brains. Surgeons have found that if points on the auditory cortex are stimulated, the sensation of sound can be produced. So we know *where* sound is consciously recognized although we know almost nothing about *how* it is recognized.

We do know that recognition of the meaning of sounds must be preceded by a process of *learning,* during which repeated exposure to sound patterns and their associated meanings conditions the cortex. A baby learns through this conditioning to recognize

185

his mother's voice, and later to associate his parents with the simple sounds "ma" and "da."

Facility in recognizing and using words develops most rapidly in the first six years of life. During these years the cortex grows in size at a very rapid rate, and this growth provides additional billions of connections between nerve fibers within which, in some mysterious way, the patterns of sound and their meanings are stored. A person stone deaf from birth has no opportunity to perceive and store these patterns. If his hearing is restored by surgery, he is at first utterly bewildered by the sounds he hears, and he must go through a painful process of learning to associate particular sounds with their meanings.

It thus appears that recognition of the teacher's question in our hypothetical classroom example occurs in a process of *matching* the message pattern provided by the brainstem with a similar pattern previously stored in the brain. The matching process must range over a huge file of stored impressions of sound meanings. In fact, the memory storage of a human adult is so great, and so deeply and permanently embedded, that it is not sufficient to point to the changes of the nerve fibers and their connections for explanation. The trillions of connections available in the brain are simply not numerous enough to provide the enormous capacity of the human memory. Physiologists suppose that memory storage may occur in the protein molecules of the neurons, which are sufficiently numerous to explain the facts of memory.

How the brain accomplishes the feat of sound recognition we do not know; but we can conceive of it as a search-and-match process. When the match is found (and the match may extend over a word, a phrase, or even a whole sentence perceived all at once) the neurons of the cortex produce a new message pattern, which starts the next process—reasoning out the answer to the question. At this point, the stimulation provided by the teacher's question rounds the corner of the brain, so to speak, and the response begins.

Recognition of the teacher's question is essentially an automatic process, which makes use of associations so well established in the experience of learning to speak that we expend no conscious effort in understanding the words. When an unfamiliar word first is presented to us ("astronaut," for example) we consciously examine its sounds and associate them with the written letters of which the word is composed. Within a short time, perhaps after using the word only a dozen times, it becomes a part of our unconscious storage of "learned" words and their meanings, automatically available for the matching process.

5. *Reasoning Out the Answer.* The next step, reasoning, is not so automatic, and it does involve conscious effort, as we are all too painfully aware. Reasoning occurs, we believe, by a process similar to recognition of meaning, but on a much more comprehensive scale. In arriving at an answer to a question, we have to search our memory for many stored data and their relations to the question.

The reasoning process is thus not a simple one-to-one association of sense messages with similar stored sound-meaning sequences. There are many intermediate steps. Many sub-messages must be formed and recognized, discarded if they do not make sense, or retained if they contribute to the answer. During the few seconds we ponder a question, literally thousands of such rational associations must be made, and dozens of these arise to consciousness, in our mind's eye, as we form the pattern of the answer.

For example, in solving the problem posed by our hypothetical teacher, the pupil needs a key noun, "force," and a verb, "balances," to associate with the noun "gravity" in the question. If he is an "A" student he won't stop there, but will embellish the answer by finding an adjective-noun phrase, "continuous change in direction," and a noun, "acceleration," to associate with the question's noun, "orbit."

All these words and phrases must be found and their logical associations built up in proper sequence, before the cortex's work is finished. During the process signals from the cortex call on many other parts of the brain to make their contribution from memory (which we believe permeates almost every part of the brain).

When the reasoning process is complete, the proper words and phrases are in the proper order to make a sentence which answers the question. But the pupil, experienced in classroom strategy, does not speak immediately. He tries the answering sentence once or twice, silently, and checks it for content and form. If the sentence is then silently recognized as suitable, and if the message center of the brain (the brainstem), which meanwhile has been keeping track of the classroom situation at large, contributes the releasing signal "ready to go," then it is time to act.

6. *The Answering Response*. Next the brain signals the outgoing nerve system to act. There are literally

dozens of instructions to be given, and acted upon in proper sequence, at this stage. From the brain down the spinal cord goes a message to the muscles of the thighs and trunk, and our pupil straightens up in his seat. Another message, with different instructions, goes to the muscles in the right arm, and it is raised. At the same time, the word-sentence message pattern is relayed to the speaking apparatus. First simple signals go to the chest muscles which cause an intake of breath. Immediately following this, the language pattern goes to work simultaneously on the muscles attached to the vocal cords, and to those which control the jaw, cheeks, and tongue. Concurrently, the pupil exhales and begins to form the words.

Suppose he is overeager and speaks before the teacher recognizes him. Even before there is time to reflect, the emotional watchdog at the message center in the brainstem flashes a signal to the cortex which, in code translation, says, "Hold up." The speaking apparatus is then *inhibited*—ready but held in check until the teacher speaks his name. Then he gives the answer: "The continuous change in direction of the orbit produces acceleration on the body of the astronaut, thus producing a force which just balances the force of gravity." Then comes the brief wait for the teacher's response, an anxious longing for the emotional and intellectual satisfaction of the single word, "Correct!"

Intelligence and Message Patterns

This brief summary of the mechanisms of natural intelligence cannot hope to convey the full scope of man's intellectual endowment, let alone reveal the rich resources of his emotional and creative life. We have glimpsed only a snapshot of the principal events that occur in the acts of knowing and reasoning in responding to a question. But our question-to-answer example suffices to illustrate the key concept of this book: Acts of intelligence are performed by the communication and manipulation of message patterns. On the route from question to answer we find sound pressure patterns, corresponding electrical impulse patterns, code translations, message patterns proliferated in ranks and echelons, matched and mismatched, sorted and selected, followed by a pattern of action messages directed to our muscles and voice apparatus, all linked in a chain of cause and effect.

The direct connection of each event in this chain with the events preceding and following it, without which the answer could not correctly respond to the question, is evidence of a second key to the nature of intelligence: logical progression from cause to effect. Answering a question is, in fact, an exercise in finding logical connections between input data and output data. Even if we had memorized the answer to the question, and no reasoning were involved, the mechanics of the stimulation-to-response chain could not proceed without correct (that is, *logically* correct) matching of the input message pattern to the stored patterns of memory.

When we "figure out" the answer, the reasoning process involves a whole organizational chart of logical connections, each of which must be satisfied by logically correct relationships, before the answer appears in our mind's eye. Reasoning consists of arranging these logical connections into a consistent pattern, discarding illogical connections that don't make sense, substituting others until a logical fit is achieved. Reasoning is a process of logical selection of a sensible order of ideas from among a vast array of nonsensible arrangements. The human brain is nature's most proficient mechanism for creating order from disorder.

All this is not to say that natural intelligence is pure logic. Far from it! Pure logic proceeds from premise to conclusion unerringly, whereas the brain proceeds for the larger part (so we believe) by trial and error, recognizing useful connections and discarding erroneous or trivial ones. But the over-all result, the correct answer to the correctly understood question, *is* logical. We can trace logically (linguists make a science of it) the connection of every word in the question to every word in the answer.

In summary, the outward signs of intelligence display logical connections between ideas, and the ideas are in turn composed of patterns of symbols arranged in accordance with the forms and rules of a language. Languages have rules for arranging symbols into groups, and the groups into larger groups, and so on, from letters to books, or from notes to symphonies. Here we need only emphasize that the chains of intelligent action, as they occur in our sense organs, nerves, brain, and muscles, are forged under similar rules. Above all, the prime function of the intelligent brain is *selection* of sense from nonsense. It must operate, when all is said and done, within the bounds of logic if it is to produce intelligent responses to the demands of the world around it.

Logic, like language, comes in various guises, pure and profane. Mathematics, which insists on strict observance of carefully defined rules, illustrates the pure form. The English language, which is infested with exceptions to general rules, exhibits profane logic. The letter combination "ough," for example, is written in just one way, but is pronounced in at least five different ways. To distinguish such spoken words as "bough" from "bow," or "dough" from "doe," the brain depends on linkages with other words; that is, on the context in which the words are used. Recognition of speech context requires a memory span that may extend over hundreds of words before the "true meaning" of a sentence or paragraph is clear.

In designing a machine to translate languages, therefore, we must take into account not only the basic words, but also the linkages between words in phrases and sentences. In Chapter 11 we shall learn how such machines deal with contexts, idioms, and the "illogical" idiosyncrasies of language. As you may guess, such machines operate by the search-and-match method we have just examined in the brain. The initial search for a match extends over a sequence of words (a phrase or an idiom); if no match is found the search is repeated with a shorter sequence. If this effort fails, a word-by-word match is sought. This last search produces a stilted translation which is far from elegant, but may nevertheless produce an intelligible result.

The process of successive searching over word patterns of shorter and shorter length illustrates how the strict logic of machine operation can be adapted to the loose logic of natural language. Most probably, the brain uses a similar narrowing-down procedure in matching the patterns of recognition and reasoning.

The On-Off Logic of a Nerve

Despite the vast complexity of the brain's operations, the basic process, communication between nerve fibers, is a most simple logical action: the choice between alternatives. Each nerve fiber, at any instant of time, is either "full on" or "full off." It is either actively passing on an electrical signal or inactively communicating nothing. So far as physiologists have been able to determine, no intermediate "partly on" condition is employed in the functioning of the nerve fibers.

How can such a simple process possibly explain the subtle variety of sense perceptions and thought? The answer lies in the trillions of connections between nerve fibers. Through these connections each fiber may be stimulated and controlled by many other fibers, and it may in turn stimulate and control still others. At the root, the action of our brain is logically simple; only in its branches does it achieve the fantastic power of the human intellect.

As we now know (in some detail!), digital electronic computers also are based on the simple "on-or-off" process; they achieve their power of artificial intelligence by assembling, transferring, comparing, displaying, and otherwise manipulating message patterns based on the numbers 0 and 1. This similarity does not mean that electronic computers are designed to imitate the human nervous system. As a matter of fact, the engineers who designed the first digital computers knew little, and cared even less, about the physiology of the brain. They wanted a machine that would compute, rapidly and accurately. Later, when workers in the life sciences began to compare notes with the computer experts, the striking similarities were realized.

In many important respects, of course, the human nervous system differs from the circuits of a computer. First, consider relative complexity. Compared with the brain, even the largest computer is simplicity itself. To cite an electronic system that even approaches the brain we can point only to the entire telephone system of the United States taken as a unit. There are about eighteen billion circuit connections in the nation's telephone system. Each of us carries around at least a trillion nerve connections!

Next, consider the speed with which the message patterns are transmitted in the two cases. The nerve transmits its electrical impulses very slowly, compared with a computer's electric circuits. Measurements show that the auditory cortex receives its first impulse, representing a sound wave, about a hundredth of a second after the sound first impinges on the eardrum. In that time, the transmission of the message patterns covers a distance of about ten inches, and the over-all velocity of the message, including all the intermediate pattern manipulations, is about 1000 inches per second. This may seem to be a pretty fast clip, but it is slow compared with a high-speed electronic computer, which passes its messages around, over distances up to several feet, in a fraction of a *millionth* of a second.

The comparison is particularly striking if we confine our attention to the travel of a particular electrical impulse along a nerve fiber compared with that in the copper conductors in a computer. The passage of electrical energy along a fast-acting nerve fiber has been measured to be about 100 meters per second. The computer wire carries its signals at better than three-tenths of the speed of light, or 100 *million* meters per second.

This fact, in itself, does not imply that the computer as a whole operates a million times faster than the nervous system, because the handling of digits by transistors and memory cores takes much more time than the mere passage of signals along the conductors. But another comparison is also of interest—the time it takes nerve fiber to get ready to transmit the next impulse, compared with that needed by a transistor. After it has completed the passage of an impulse, the nerve must have a resting period before it can again be stimulated to turn itself "on" and transmit another impulse. This "refractory" period of rest, even in the fastest-acting nerves, lasts about a thousandth of a second. In contrast, a fast-acting computer transistor, having completed the transmission of one impulse, is ready for the next in a few billionths of a second. Here, again, we encounter a time factor of about a million in favor of the computer over the nerve network. The memory cells in computers (magnetic cores and films) are not so fast, but even they can be "cycled" in a few millionths of a second.

We find, then, that the human nervous system is incomparably more complex than any computer, but is also considerably more sluggish in its handling of messages. This is a crucial factor in designing machines to imitate the brain, because we can trade speed against complexity. The brain can bring into play, in performing an act of intelligence, tens of thousands of nerve-fiber chains simultaneously. The computer, on the other hand, uses its "fiber-chains" (circuits of transistors, conductors, and memory cells) one after the other, as the sequences of digits follow the computation plan. Only in limited ways are groups of computer parts used simultaneously. The computer makes up for its one-at-a-time operation by its million-times speed advantage, which puts it (for certain tasks) on a more nearly equal footing with the brain.

This near equality exists, of course, only when the brain and the computer are performing the same problem. The comparison takes no account whatever of the time required to *prepare* the machine to compute its problem. To compose the computation plan for solving problems in mathematical logic, for example, may take months of intensive effort, whereas the equivalent learning process in the brain can occur in a few days of similarly intensive work. The advantage of the computer, in performing the tasks of artificial intelligence, thus depends on the pattern of work to be accomplished. Only when there is a very large amount of a particular kind of work to be done, sufficient to justify the cost of preparing and executing the program, can we afford to use machinery. Otherwise, the magnificently versatile brain brooks no competition.

Nerve Electricity—A Closer Look

We conclude this chapter with some further aspects of nerve electricity, useful in understanding the functions of machine intelligence. This is a fascinating subject in itself, and the interested reader is referred for further information to the excellent book in the Science Study Series by Dr. Robert Galambos.* Nerves come in many sizes. They vary in length from a fraction of a millimeter to more than a meter. The diameter of a nerve fiber in the human system is very small, 1 to 20 microns (1 micron is a thousandth of a millimeter). Despite its tiny size, nerve physiologists have been able to explore the interior structure of the fiber. They find that nerve cells are in fact living batteries, which charge themselves during periods of rest and discharge when they are stimulated. When charged, the cell has a voltage of about 70 millivolts (about 1/20th the voltage of a flashlight battery). This potential difference† results from concentrations of electrically charged atoms, the positive potassium ion $K+$ and the positive sodium ion $Na+$.

An invisible membrane (not yet seen through a microscope, and hence one of the primary articles of faith in nerve physiology) is believed to surround the inner part of the nerve cell. This membrane, it is supposed, governs the flow of the ions. In the rest period the cell charges itself by pumping $K+$ ions through the membrane into the inside of the cell, until there are, in a given volume, about twenty times as many $K+$ ions inside the cell as outside. During this time, the membrane also prevents the

* See Robert Galambos, *Nerves and Muscles* (Doubleday & Company, Science Study Series, 1962).

† This 70-millivolt difference in electric potential seems to be a constant of nature, since it appears in all electrically active cells, nerves, and muscles, in all forms of animal and plant life.

Na+ ions (in the fluid surrounding the membrane) from getting inside. It takes only a thousandth of a second for this charging process to be completed. At this stage, the difference in the concentrations of the two types of ions, on either side of the membrane, produces the 70-millivolts potential difference previously mentioned.

The charged cell may then continue to rest in its charged condition for some time, so long as it is not called upon to carry a nerve impulse. But when it is stimulated (by another nerve fiber) a dramatic change occurs. The membrane is believed to change radically its control of the K+ and Na+ ions. First, it allows the Na+ ions to pour into the inside of the cell, thus neutralizing the effect of the sodium charge concentration. Second, less than a thousandth of a second later, the membrane allows the K+ ions to leak rapidly to the outside. The combination of these two ion movements actually reverses the electric charge of the cell, which momentarily becomes 20 millivolts negative.

This momentary change in the cell potential constitutes the nerve impulse (Fig. 48). It lasts (typically) only a thousandth of a second. Thereafter, the flow of Na+ and K+ ions is reversed, sodium being pumped out and potassium pumped in, until the 70-millivolt resting potential is restored. During the recharging period the cell membrane does not respond to any further stimulation; it is in the "refractory" condition previously mentioned.

These events occur at the particular point at which the nerve fiber is stimulated. As we might expect, they are not confined long to that precise

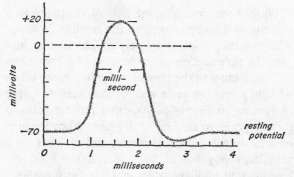

FIG. 48. Plot of a nerve impulse against time. Human nerve pulses last about one-thousandth of a second, whereas typical computer pulses last only a few billionths of a second.

spot on the nerve fiber. When the ions move (ions in motion constitute an electric current) they set up currents in the adjacent portions of the membrane, which react just as if they had been stimulated by another nerve fiber. The reaction proceeds along the membrane "like a prairie fire" (to use Dr. Galambos' descriptive term). At each successive point on the fiber, the ebb and flow of K+ and Na+ ions occurs, and the 20-millivolt impulse flows along until it reaches the end of the nerve fiber.

If, as is usual, the fiber branches out, the impulse flows into each of the branches and the several impulses thus formed proceed until they meet their junction points ("synapses") with still other fibers. In this manner, a single impulse may be proliferated into uncounted thousands of new impulses which flow simultaneously to the far reaches of the brain and spinal cord.

199

We can see now why the flow of electricity in a nerve is so sluggish, compared to electricity in wires. Although the analogies are very rough, we can compare the nerve action to the burning of a fuse, electric conduction to the flow of water in a hose. When we light a fuse, we must wait for the chemical action of burning to be passed on, from powder grain to powder grain, to the end of the fuse. When we turn on a hose (assuming it is already full of water, as a wire is already full of free electrons), we do not have to wait until the water entering the hose flows to the nozzle. Subject to the delays due to compressibility of air bubbles and elastic expansion of the hose, the water in the nozzle moves out at almost the same instant that the water from the faucet moves in. Similarly, free electrons entering a wire need not flow to the end for an impulse to be transmitted. The impulse is transmitted, almost with the speed of light, by the forces between the electrons. The electrons themselves drift along the wire at a leisurely gait.

One final facet of nerve electricity demands attention: the fact that, as nerve fibers can be excited by impulses from other nerve fibers, they also can be prevented from responding by "inhibiting" impulses from other fibers. The situation can be made clear if you think of a set of several "input" nerve fibers, all terminating on a single fiber which is to produce, or fail to produce, an impulse of its own (Fig. 49). Every nerve operates either in the "full-on" condition or the "full-off." It does not go into action, full on, unless the excitation it receives equals or exceeds a certain voltage, known as the

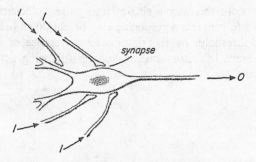

FIG. 49. One nerve may be stimulated (or inhibited) by many others. Shown are four input pulses which produce one output pulse. If all inputs are required simultaneously to produce the output, this is the equivalent of an "and" circuit with four inputs.

excitation "threshold." Suppose, then, that the excitation from any one of the several input fibers is below the threshold value. The following fiber is not excited by any one of its input fibers. But if two of the input fibers act at the same instant, and if the *sum* of their exciting voltages exceeds the threshold value, then excitation occurs. Similarly, it may take three input excitations at once, or more, to exceed the threshold. In this manner, the relative timing of the impulses, as well as their strength, becomes a critical factor.

Needless to say, this complication greatly enlarges the variety of events that can occur at the junction of several nerve fibers. Nor is this the end of the matter. Certain nerve fibers can generate "inhibitory" potentials, which counteract the normal "excitatory" pulses delivered at the same time by other fibers. In this way a single large pulse, sufficient in itself to generate a response, may be cut down below the threshold, by the simultaneous presence of one or more inhibitory pulses—and no following action occurs.

CHAPTER 10

THE MANY FACES OF INTELLIGENCE

> To me "intelligence" seems to denote little more
> than the complex of performances we happen to
> respect, but do not understand. . . . But we should
> not let our inability to discern a locus of intelligence
> lead us to conclude that programmed computers
> therefore cannot think. For it may be so with man,
> as with machine, that when we finally understand
> the structure and program, the feeling of mystery
> (and self-approbation) will weaken.
>
> —DR. MARVIN MINSKY

What is artificial intelligence? For that matter, what
is natural intelligence? Without reasonable answers
to these questions, my purpose in writing this book
and your purpose in reading it can hardly be served.
These are not easy questions. Some philosophers
insist that the question "What is intelligence?" cannot be answered rigorously because no one can "get
outside himself" and observe his behavior objectively while at the same time experiencing it sub-
jectively.

My abridged dictionary defines intelligence simply as "ability to reason and understand." These

few words hardly express the fullness of the concept. Even the big dictionaries skirt around an all-pervading personal attribute of human intelligence, *consciousness*. We make constant use of our intelligence to express our purposes and our needs, as well as to learn, to reflect upon, and use our knowledge. Most of these activities are directed from within, presided over by the inner awareness of the ego. So, firmly intertwined in the idea of intelligence, is the first concept of them all—knowledge of self.

It is at this point that the difficulty with "artificial intelligence" begins. For we have no evidence that any computer, however powerful in structure or elegant in program, has any consciousness of itself. So, if intelligence must connote self-consciousness, no machine presently known can be called intelligent.

But, if we define intelligence on an objective basis, by observing the actions of intelligent beings, we may argue on different grounds. When a machine earns the respect of an intelligent human being with whom it communicates or competes (as the Model 7094 computer did in its checkers game with champion Nealey) it may merit the adjective "intelligent" wholly on the argument of observed performance. The fact that the 7094 computer could not "know" it was "intelligent" (that is, well-programmed) is then beside the point. It is sufficient that the computer performed in an intelligent manner.

But is it? From the behavior described in the earlier chapters of this book, we know in general what the 7094 computer does, and in the next chapter we can be more explicit about checkers. Do such operations earn any computer the right of admission to the world of the intellect? This question has generated a great debate, one of the most significant in the modern history of philosophy and technology.

In this chapter we shall explore the forms of behavior—by humans, animals, and machines—on which the arguments turn. In particular, we will identify two principal types of intelligence that are alike in that both involve learning, but are different in their relation to the teaching process. The first, adaptive intelligence, is exhibited by a student who learns only what he is taught by his teachers and by other experiences. The second, creative intelligence, is shown by the student who, taking leave of his teachers and the world as he finds it, strikes out on his own. The behavior of creative intelligence is exhibited by those who discover or invent new knowledge, new art, new philosophy. The question whether a machine can display creative intelligence is the end point of this book (Chapter 12). But before we can attack it, we must define our terms. As background for our definitions, it will be helpful to review the man-versus-machine argument that has raged for decades.

Man versus Machine

Of all the natural endowments of man none is more highly prized or more fiercely defended than his gift of superior intelligence. Certainly, there is no other explanation of man's domination of "his" planet. The conquest of one culture over another, the winning of wars (even victory in a football game), all are ascribed to the superior intelligence of the victor. From Homer to last night's TV documentary—throughout all recorded history—the vision and cunning of the human mind have held the center of the stage.

Also evident since tribal days is the primordial fear of an intelligence superior to man's. The gods of nearly all the primitive religions were all-knowing and vengeful. Invention of the first tool added to this fear of the supernatural another abiding concern: that man might someday be overcome by his own creations. As tools became more powerful (and especially as the machines of the Industrial Revolution have become more complex) this concern has kept pace with man's intellectual development. The older, simpler superstitions have given way to more sophisticated fears.

Today the same concern is centered on the intelligent machinery of computer science. Few people take the threat seriously. After all, one can always pull out the computer's power plug. But the nagging idea that a computer might someday develop a will of its own, and put its power plug back is the modern version of an ancient superstition.

The man-versus-machine argument has waxed with particular fervor during the last one hundred years. In the last century, Samuel Butler wrote, "There is no security against the ultimate development of mechanical consciousness in the fact of machines possessing little consciousness now." Butler put the matter squarely when he imagined that the time might come when "man shall become to the machine what the horse and dog are to us." In his day, the available machinery gave little support to his speculations. But then came the digital electronic computer, circa 1943.* In a mere twenty years of intense work on the design and programming of these machines, man finds himself for the first time in possession of the means to imitate logical thought . . . and the fat is back in the fire.

The coining of the term "artificial intelligence" in the 1950s was the signal for a particularly acrimonious expression of conflicting ideas. The defenders of intelligent machinery predicted rapid progress in the intellectual attainments of computer programs. The detractors were equally vigorous in denying that the word "intelligent" was then, or ever could be, properly applied to any machine.

Most important, as the debate has raged, a small group of dedicated mathematicians and philosophers have been at work, attempting to find out what actually can be done and to discover the general principles that will define the ultimate limits of machine intelligence. These men are fond of quoting Leonardo da Vinci who, five hundred years ago, wrote, "The bird is an instrument working according to natural law, which instrument is within the capacity of man to reproduce in all its movements." Though a jet aircraft does not use all the "movements" of a bird, the same combinations of updraft

---

* Charles Babbage (1792–1871) anticipated virtually all of the basic concepts of modern electronic computer technology in his "Analytical Engine." This was a very complicated mechanical device designed to store and manipulate numbers in much the same manner as present-day computers. The British government provided support for his work, but his plans were too ambitious for the technology of his day, and his engine was never completed. An excellent account of this early work is contained in the book, *Faster than Thought,* edited by B. V. Bowden (Sir Isaac Pitman & Sons, London, 1957, pp. 6–23).

and aerodynamic lift support the aircraft and sea-gull. And the aircraft certainly shows that, in the field of locomotion, man can devise machines that out-perform all natural creatures (including himself) by a very substantial margin. Only when the jealously held faith in the innate superiority of man's *mind* is challenged do we find disbelief and fear.

Researchers in artificial intelligence are also quick to point out, with wry expression, that as each new advance in programming is reported and explained the doubters retreat to higher ground. This progres-sive removal of the machine's accomplishments from the area of debate has been recognized by J. P. Eckert (who, with J. W. Mauchly, was responsible for the design of ENIAC, the first digital electronic computer). Says Dr. Eckert, "After seventeen years, I've finally been forced to adopt the definition that thinking is what computers cannot do. This defini-tion is very workable, since it changes from year to year as computer progress is made."

Dr. Eckert's observation brings into focus the ul-timate question: How far will computer progress go? Only a few first halting steps have been taken, but these have occurred, for the most part, in only ten years—and the pace of discovery is rapidly ac-celerating. Given this recent history, everyone can find occasion for thought. Is there an intellectual revolution in the making? Can the machines of computation and logic possibly exert effects on so-ciety like those of the machines of power that brought on the Industrial Revolution?

Natural Intelligence Defined

Our first task in defining machine intelligence is to bound the limits of the word "intelligence" as it is ordinarily understood. For a start, we quote the appropriate definition† from Webster's New International Dictionary, Unabridged; it says: "Intelligence: 1.(a) the ability to learn or understand from experience; ability to acquire and retain knowledge; mental ability; (b) the ability to respond quickly and successfully to a new situation; use of the faculty of reason in solving problems, directing conduct, etc., effectively; (c) in psychology, measured success in using these abilities to perform certain tasks."

The dictionary's words are carefully chosen, and we do well to measure our estimate of an intelligent man or woman against them. Let us consider an acquaintance whom we rate as highly intelligent, and ask how we know he is a "real brain." Under (a) of the definition, he must show that he can *learn,* that is, *recognize, store,* and *organize* information. He must be able to achieve *understanding;* that is, *relate* his stored knowledge to the facts and fancies of the world around him. Under (b), he must show mental adaptability; that is, ability to deviate from past patterns and find new ones as needed. Also under (b) he must be effective and active in using his brain. This quality he will show

† The five other definitions in this dictionary deal with "information," that is, the *content* of intelligent actions, rather than with the capabilities of intelligent beings. These concepts, while basic to the full development of the subject, are apart from our immediate concern.

by his ability to solve problems for which he has no previous special preparation, and by his ability to direct his own actions, to follow directions, and to lead the conduct of others. Under (c) he will display a mental age (as revealed by intelligence tests) which measures well above average; he will almost certainly have an I.Q. above 120.

Note that all these attributes are measured by observation. We judge a man's intelligence by his words and deeds. The core of the argument for artificial intelligence lies in the fact that computer systems can be observed, by *their* words and deeds, to behave in similar ways. A machine can learn. It can respond (when programmed with sufficient sophistication) to a new situation. It can solve problems. It can direct conduct (as in oil refineries and space explorations; all astronauts are guided in the first, critical miles of take-off by computers that observe and correct the trajectory of the space vehicle). It can even answer certain questions from standard intelligence tests. In these matters, the observed behavior of computers and men differ not in *kind,* but in *degree.*

Those who argue against the idea of artificial intelligence do not deny the validity of these observations of similar behavior. But they insist that the similarity is confined to the end results of problem solving; they question whether the methods of mind and machine can be compared at all. There is, they insist, a world of difference between the conscious striving of man's intellect and the blind mechanistic manipulation of symbols in a computer program. They point out that man must make the computer program and interpret the results. They agree that computers can be intellectual tools of great aid to the human mind. But that they have any standing as intelligent beings in themselves—that they can compete with the human mind on an equal footing—no. Even the apparently contrary evidence of the 7094 computer defeating champion Nealey is dismissed as not significant, because it took a very brilliant (and very patient) man to think out the program for checker-playing.

Dr. Samuel himself, while admitting that his program can consistently defeat his own mind in that game, insists that his computer could never out-think him in planning the grand strategy of the program itself. He feels that the programmer must always, inevitably, work with abstractions of greater power than those he puts into his program.

Certainly this qualification is true of his work, and of the work of every other contemporary master programmer. For each new routine mastered by a computer, however elaborate and powerful, a still more elaborate and powerful routine has been developed, and used, in the mind of man. Many, perhaps most, computer philosophers agree with Dr. Samuel that this must always be so.

But not all computer scientists agree. Several of the "positivists" point out that Dr. Samuel's own work has proved the superiority of a machine in the particular job it was programmed to do; and they ask why a computer cannot write its own program, using its own higher abstractions. One of the outstanding teams of research men in this field, Newell, Shaw, and Simon, believe it can; and their work has gone far to show how it might be done. They are master heuristicians, and their program for the General Problem Solver (Chapter 12) rates with Dr. Samuel's work as a great milestone on the road to machine intelligence.

We take leave of this debate by returning to our question: Is there an intellectual revolution in the making? We can shed light on this question if we observe that it matters little that the programmer is (perhaps must be) ahead of his machine, so long as the machine is ahead of its user. The automobile is the creature of its designers in Detroit, but the housewife needs to know nothing about its design. She can use it to achieve feats of locomotion unattainable without it. That is an achievement of the Industrial Revolution.

In the same sense, checkers champion Nealey could use the 7094 computer to defeat human opponents whom he could not defeat himself (however unsportsmanlike this would be). In another sense, when Newell and Simon's logic theory program (to prove simple theorems of symbolic logic) was able, in fifty-two tries, to find even one proof shorter and more elegant than those given in the classic treatise *Principia Mathematica,* it scored a victory of competitive intelligence. Since brevity and elegance are points on which the tournaments of mathematics are scored, this isolated instance is a notable straw in the wind. These examples, and there are others, are the early achievements of the intellectual revolution.

Real versus Apparent Intelligence

Before we can define artificial intelligence, we must accept the fact that any workable definition will be written in terms of the machine's observed performance. Superficial observation in this field of inquiry, as in most others, can be highly misleading. So we must devise definitive tests that will help to distinguish between "real" intelligence and the "mere appearance" of intelligence.

Take, for example, the often-quoted definition: "Artificial intelligence: Behavior by a machine that, if exhibited by a human, would be called intelligent." Without further qualification, this simple and attractive definition can lead to much confusion. If we did not know how the high-fidelity phonograph works we might think it intelligent because it exhibits a highly intelligent form of human behavior, the ability to speak meaningfully. But the phonograph, as we happen to know, merely reproduces the unalterable pattern of speech waveforms embedded in the grooves of its record. It is not designed to make any contribution whatever to the form or the content of its recorded message. Quite to the contrary, it is designed to avoid any such contribution; that is, to be as faithful as possible in reproducing its input data without change.

Such rote recitation, however "human" in form, can hardly qualify as intelligence. But if a phonograph existed that did make a significant contribution to its message (for example, if it was observed translating prose into poetry), we might feel that it deserved the approbation "creatively intelligent." Similarly, if we observed a machine translating Russian into English, we might be tempted to attribute "intelligence" to it. But we might be wrong, at least in certain respects that we shall consider later.

How, then, can we test a machine's intelligence? One approach is to provide some unanticipated variation in its input data, carefully contrived to reveal whether the machine can adapt, that is, whether it can *learn from its experience.* We take this italicized phrase from Webster's definition of natural intelligence and use it in constructing our definition of artificial intelligence.

We must, of course, be explicit about what we mean by "learn from experience" as applied to a machine. We recall (from Chapter 9) the functions of the brain. In learning, we human beings recognize and remember, through repeated exposure, patterns in our environment. We assign meanings to these patterns and organize them into new ones, having more comprehensive implications, by noting similarities and differences, accepting logical relations, rejecting illogical ones. In the end, by relying on logical organization and reorganization of generalized information patterns, we build a body of stored knowledge which we use in reasoning and acting.

Machine learning, however different in the detailed methods employed, is the same. A machine that possesses the ability to recognize, store, recall, and manipulate patterns of information and to organize and reorganize these patterns into new, more comprehensive, or more meaningful patterns is *by definition* a machine that learns from its environment.

The first key to testing for machine intelligence, then, is to test for ability to organize information. The phonograph will fail this test. It merely repeats information. Our program to compute π will fail it. All the organization is provided in the program; the 225 computer did not alter the program within itself. It was not *programmed* to learn.

Many computer programs, particularly those designed for playing games and solving problems, will pass the learning test. One of the surest clues appears when the machine is able to deal with patterns of input information (such as moves in checkers, instructions to prove theorems or to recognize pictures) which the programmer did not explicitly foresee. The machine with this ability must adapt its program to the specific patterns applied to it, within the more general framework of the problem area for which it is programmed. It must be able not only to organize data within itself but also to adapt to changes in its environment.

These are not easy concepts, and perhaps we should expand upon them with some examples. First let us deal with apparent intelligence, behavior that only appears to involve learning because no adaptation to the environment is involved. We take our first example from the animal world.

The Apparent Intelligence of the Wasp

Among living creatures other than man the most impressive examples of apparent intelligence occur in the insects. The ability of ants, wasps, and bees to organize their societies, to communicate the direction of distant sources of food, to act in concert against enemies, is truly impressive. For centuries these insects were believed to possess the ability to learn and reason. But patient testing by animal psychologists has proved this belief to be an illusion. The social insects have very limited ability to learn, and their complex behavior is entirely explained by instinct, the inheritance of adaptation amassed over

215

uncounted millions of generations. The adult insect in his own generation is unable to adapt, in any complex way, to a new, unforeseen situation.

A convincing illustration of this inability to adapt is seen in experimentation with the adult female Sphex wasp. This wasp, when she is about to lay her eggs, has the unvarying habit of stinging a cricket to paralyze it, but not kill it. She places the cricket in a burrow, lays her eggs beside it, and departs. When the eggs hatch, the grubs feed on the still-living cricket. Very intelligent behavior—on superficial examination. But under the scrutiny of a test for adaptation, it proves to be apparent intelligence only. The wasp, it turns out, can operate in no other way. She is repeating, by rote, a pattern that is permanently and unalterably "wired" in a fixed program within her brain.

A crucial test concerns an incidental detail in the wasp's behavior. Before dragging the cricket into the burrow, she leaves it at the entrance and enters the burrow for an inspection. Then she hauls the cricket inside. If this routine is interrupted in any way, she goes back and starts over again from the point of interruption. Let an experimenter move the cricket a few inches away from the entrance of the burrow while the wasp is inside making her inspection. On emerging from the burrow the wasp will not drag the cricket inside from its new location. She drags it to the entrance only, then goes inside and makes her inspection all over again. She does not remember that she already has accomplished that part of her routine. Only if she finds the cricket at the entrance, can she proceed in her accustomed manner.

Psychologists, hoping to find some slight evidence

of ability to adapt, have moved the cricket away from the entrance as many as forty times, but the wasp never realizes (even after forty repeated inspections of the burrow) that she could stop all this nonsense and be done with it.

A rat, on the contrary, would figure out this kind of problem in short order. Rats can learn in such circumstances; they (with apes, dogs, horses, and porpoises) are among the most able learners and adapters in the animal kingdom. The programs in their brains are flexible—not permanently wired— and they can easily pass the tests of adaptability.

Among machines we find an interesting (and astonishing) case of apparent intelligence in the computer system that translates Russian automatically into English. On first examination, before we know the way in which it is programmed, this computer system would appear to be highly intelligent. It seems to make a distinct contribution to the form (if not the content) of the information passing through it. This is indeed a sophisticated example of computer technology, the first in a line of machines that we can hope will eventually topple the Tower of Babel. It is potentially a most important aid to man's intellect.

The machine's intelligence, however, is largely of the apparent variety. When we examine its inner workings, as we shall in the next chapter, we find that while it organizes information in certain ways, it cannot adapt. It follows a program of reorganizing the input phrases and comparing them with stored translated phrases. It is a "table-look-up" machine, a kind of automatic dictionary-reader that is hardly more intelligent than the Sphex wasp.

To test the translating computer we alter the sequence of its input sentences in Russian, in a linguistically significant way, and examine the English translation to see whether the linguistic clues have been detected and acted upon. The routine does not change, because it cannot; the process of translation was not programmed to adapt to such changes.

The human translator, asked to make a fine distinction in meaning, will resort to new words or new sentence structure, or introduce a telling idiom. The translating machine can do this only in very limited ways, as the quality of its translation shows. Before machine translation of human quality can be accomplished, adaptive translation programs must be devised.

Tests for Adaptive Intelligence

The challenge presented to the Sphex wasp, when the experimenter moved the paralyzed cricket, gives us the clue to the type of "psychological testing" needed to show whether a machine has adaptive intelligence. The test must apply some sort of unanticipated change in the computer's input data. The machine's response then is observed and scored on its ability to deal "successfully" with the data pattern, the "success" being measured against some standard. What standard? Well, since such machines are designed to assist in, or even take over, man's intellectual labors, what better standard than man's reaction to the same unanticipated data pattern?

This criterion leads to the notion of placing the machine in direct competition with a human being who is using his wits. If the machine can outwit its human opponent, even occasionally, we have evidence of adaptive intelligence. The evidence may be misleading—only a detailed examination of the computer's program will show whether self-organization and adaptation are actually present—but it will seem plausible until tests of the program proper prove otherwise. As Dr. Samuel says, "The ability to have the program play against human opponents adds spice to the study and, incidentally, provides a convincing demonstration for those who do not believe that machines can learn."

In the present state of the art such man-versus-machine competitions must be confined to a particular game or to a particular type of problem (plane geometry, or symbolic logic, or symbolic integration—but only one at a time). We can define a competition, however, which will clarify the basic principles. We may, in fact, imagine a contest in which a machine in competition with a man is asked to answer any question in any field.

The late A. M. Turing, one of the foremost contributors to the theory of machine computation, laid down the rules for such a contest. In Turing's test, a man of high intelligence (the Examiner) asks questions and receives answers over a teletypewriter circuit. At the other end of the circuit a man answering the questions with human intelligence operates the teletypewriter part of the time. But during the remaining time a machine answers the questions. The Examiner knows that the answers come from either man or machine, but he has no clue as to which. His task is to identify the source of each answer. Did it come from the man or from the machine?

The Examiner has a free choice of questions. He may pose questions he feels certain are not answerable by any machine. With a little practice, he will identify correctly the source of the answer on almost every question. But not necessarily on *every* question. His score of incorrect identifications is taken as a measure of the "intelligence" of the machine. The fewer times the Examiner is wrong, the less intelligent the machine. So far, no one has played this rather farfetched game. Its purpose, as is so often the case in similar devices employed in philosophy, is to *define* a method of measurement and to bound its limits.

Suppose the Examiner in such a test should ask, "Can you prove to me the theorem that the bisector of an angle is equidistant from the sides of the angle?" The answer comes back, "Erect perpendiculars to the sides, coterminous at the bisector, forming two right triangles. The right triangles are congruent, since they have one side in common and two equal angles at the vertex. The perpendiculars are equal since corresponding elements of congruent triangles are equal. Q.E.D."

Suppose, further, that the answer did not come back for fifteen minutes. This is rather a long time for so simple a proof. So the Examiner could imagine that a computer might be involved, or perhaps a man who was very rusty on geometry, and he would then guess the source. But if the answer came back after a pause of only twenty seconds, he would conclude, reasonably, that he must be dealing with a fast-thinking man. He then would be almost certain that his guess should be, "Man answering." But he could be wrong, because this proof of the theorem was devised in 0.32 minute by the Gelernter geometry-theorem proving program on an IBM 704 Computer. Of course, a knowledgeable and adroit Examiner would stay away from a question like this, knowing that a computer might be able to handle it. But an unwary Examiner could be fooled, especially if he were out of touch with the latest achievements in problem-solving computer programs.

Turing's test leads us closer to our definition of artificial intelligence by emphasizing the ability to answer specific questions posed from a general area of inquiry. Perhaps we can agree that if a computer can answer in this game just one question not explicitly foreseen, organizing its information, and adapting its program to do so, it rates one mark for an intelligent act.

Creative Intelligence

Having recognized the adaptive aspect of artificial intelligence in the ability to answer specific questions posed from within a more general area of inquiry, we can hardly refrain from taking the next step. What about the ability to ask a significant question that points outside the established framework of known answers? Here we take leave of adaptive learning and enter the world of discovery, the world of the creative intellect.

To learn we need only to understand ("adapt to") what we are taught. But to use in constructive ways what we have learned we must ask the right questions, particularly, "Is that so?", "Why?", and that most powerful question, "What if?"

The person who makes a habit of asking questions

221

worth answering has gone beyond mere learning. He has graduated, taken leave of the curriculum, embarked on adventures of his own. Every great teacher, artist, discoverer, inventor, researcher, recognizes the limits of his art or science, and asks questions that will, if answered, push back those limits.

The drive to wrestle with the proper subjects and objects of curiosity, without which the creative pursuits of man could not exist, is extremely difficult even to discuss in terms of computer science. For one thing, the urge to invent, or discover, or produce a work of art, is a conscious urge based on powerful emotion. No machine, as we have said, is known to have consciousness of itself; without consciousness it can hardly possess the emotion of curiosity. This does not mean that a machine cannot be creative. For if we include *exploration*—the finding of new, significant patterns, previously unrecognized—in the domain of intellectual creativity, then indeed machines can compete with human beings in the asking and answering of worthwhile questions.

If such creative ability exists in a machine, Turing's test will not reveal it, because the questions are posed by the human Examiner. The machine needs only to prove that, having learned its lesson, it can answer a question to which it has not previously been exposed. To test for creative intelligence we must in some way assign the task of *questioning* to the machine. We must devise a conjugate form of Turing's test. Not an easy job, but the following test, while lacking the beautiful symmetry of Turing's procedure, may perhaps suggest the means and will offer an example.

Suppose that at one end of the teletypewriter circuit we have an Examiner who is a good judge of creative thought in general, while at the other end we have a man possessing creative intelligence (perhaps as evidenced by his discoveries in science or his works of art) and a machine we desire to test for creative intelligence.

The Examiner types out the following instruction: "Pose to me a question and suggest the means of finding the answer." He must judge whether the question and approach to a solution came from the man or the machine.

The Examiner will have various clues. He knows that the man at the other end has been instructed to compete; that is, to pose questions and solutions that will impress the Examiner with the depth of his knowledge and his intellectual curiosity. If the question is trivial or simpleminded the Examiner will tend to identify it as coming from the machine, but he runs the risk that the creative man at the other end has underestimated the machine's creative powers and, being lazy, has attempted to score a point with a simple question. So, as in Turing's test, the Examiner can make a mistake. If, in many judgments of questions and suggested avenues of solution the Examiner makes even one mistake, that error may be taken as one mark of creative intelligence in a machine, objectively measured.

If Turing's test seems farfetched, this conjugate test is farther fetched. It serves perhaps only to illustrate the difficulty of measuring creative intelligence objectively. But it opens the way for an example. Suppose that to the Examiner's request for a question and a method of solution this reply comes back: *"Question:* Given the equation $x^n + y^n = z^n$, where x, y, and z are whole numbers, how would you go about proving that there are no values of x, y, and z for which this equation is true, when n is an integer greater than 2?"

This is Fermat's last theorem, one of the most famous in mathematics, which has never been proved‡ despite intense efforts by number theorists of every generation since it was first posed in 1637. It thus qualifies as an excellent "creative" question in number theory, one that a creative computing machine as well as an educated man might well be familiar with.

Now consider two possible proposed avenues of solution. Suppose the reply was, "I would use a computer to test all possible cases by inserting 3, 4, 5, etc., for n, and all the non-zero integers for x, y, and z." This proposal for solution is simpleminded, because no matter how large the numbers the computer used, it could never prove by mere trial that the next larger numbers would not make the two sides of the equation equal. A knowledgeable man would realize this and avoid suggesting this approach. So the Examiner would be safe in guessing that this proposal came "from the machine."

Suppose, however, that the reply suggested the obtaining of partial proofs by analysis of the properties of prime numbers, which is the principal ap-

‡ The effort to prove this theorem has not been lessened by the fact that Fermat wrote in the margin of a book, "I have discovered a truly remarkable proof, which this margin is too small to contain." Partial proofs (for certain values of n, for example) abound, but the fact that no complete proof has been found, says the Encyclopædia Britannica, "is one of the most amazing facts in mathematics."

proach used by number theorists. The Examiner would have to decide then whether any machine could be programmed to ask such a good question and have such a knowledgeable approach. As things now stand, he would be safe in guessing that only a man would be capable of such a response. But if a machine§ *did* so respond, his wrong guess would be a measure of its creative intelligence.

Artificial Intelligence Defined

Now we are ready to define artificial intelligence by reference to the observations and tests outlined in the preceding pages: "Artificial Intelligence: (a) The ability of machines to organize information into meaningful patterns; ability to recognize, store, recall, and manipulate such patterns in playing games, solving problems, answering questions, etc., and in controlling the actions of other mechanisms; (b) the ability of a machine to adapt to its environment, particularly to respond to patterns of stimulation not explicitly foreseen in its design; (c) the observed performance of such machines, as measured by comparison with, or in competition against, human intelligence."

In the next chapter we describe some machines covered, in varying degrees, by this hard-won definition. In so doing we run into heavy weather. We find that almost *all* the computer applications fail to qualify as "intelligent" under (a) or (b) of the definition—useful, yes, beyond the fondest dreams of

§ Of course, we must rule out in this exercise any machine that is only apparently creative, that is, one that has a store of questions and proposed solutions which it repeats by rote.

Eckert and Mauchly. Computers save time and tedium almost beyond comprehension, but *intelligent,*
in the sense of being able to answer questions not
explicitly foreseen? Not proved for the great majority of them.

CHAPTER 11

FOUR INTELLIGENT MACHINES

> A computer does what it is told, and it is no criti-
> cism of it to say that it cannot be told how to do the
> work of a Prime Minister or write a good poem.
> How far a computer can go in performing what
> are ordinarily regarded as intellectual tasks is not
> clear—it depends on what processes can be clearly
> described.—SIR EDWARD BULLARD

How do machines manipulate the symbols of
thought? How do they deal with words and questions, with mathematical concepts, with human competition? To answer these questions we now take up
four "intelligent" computer systems. The first was
designed to translate Russian into English, the second to answer questions about baseball, the third to
prove theorems in symbolic logic, and the fourth to
play the game of checkers. Together they illustrate
mechanisms and programs that put into practice the
concepts of the preceding chapter.

A Machine that Translates

At the input to the translation machine we find a
teletypewriter whose keys bear the symbols of the

Russian language. The typist does not know the language, but she is familiar with the Russian characters and can copy, key by key, the Russian text. Issuing from her typewriter is a punched paper tape, which passes directly to the tape-reader of the computer. At the output of the computer another teletypewriter chatters away, printing out an English translation. The computer connecting the two typewriters is not a general-purpose machine and it cannot do any other work. But it can produce, most of the time, an intelligible translation.

Stored within its memory is an "electronic dictionary" containing more than 100,000 Russian phrases, words, and parts of words, with their English equivalents. The computer is a search-and-match machine. It compares the machine code from its input typewriter with the stored codes in its dictionary. When it finds a match it types out the equivalent English.

Thus baldly stated, the performance of this machine seems simple enough. But, having spent some time in this book studying the structure of natural language, we are well prepared to realize that automatic translation is far from simple. The translation machine must be prepared to accept more than the stereotyped forms of computer language. It must deal with the endless variety of natural speech and, at the same time, adjust the conflicting rules of two types of speech. That any machine could do this would, only twenty years ago, have been judged highly improbable, if not downright impossible.

The essential task in machine translation is to recognize the proper meaning in the input language and to render that meaning in the output language.

This undertaking involves far more than recognizing individual words, because words usually have more than one definition and more than one use. For example, the word "state" in my unabridged dictionary has nineteen definitions as a noun, four as an adjective, and three as a transitive verb. How can a machine, if it works with only one word at a time, possibly distinguish among these twenty-six possibilities? It cannot. This is one of the few tasks which the experts label "impossible." Word-for-word translation is, by and large, incomprehensible.

Rather, the machine must do what humans do. It must consider groups of words—phrases—each word of which contributes to the proper meaning. The machine must, in fact, provide a memory span that extends over many words, and it must (if it can) recognize the words as a group. The longer the span of the phrase, the more certain is the identification of its meaning.

When we deal with a group of words, the number of different possibilities becomes enormously greater as the number of words in the group increases. We have already noted that there are 17,576 (26^3) possible three-*letter* combinations, only 400 of which are common English words. There are a billion billion (10^{18}) possible three-*word* combinations among the million definitions in the English language. Most of these make no sense, of course, but millions of them are meaningful phrases. When we consider phrases of more than three words, the situation becomes rapidly very much worse.

How can a machine deal with such complexity? The answer is found in a routine we already have examined; that is, by storage of defined phrases.

What is needed for machine translation is a mechanical dictionary that contains groups of words, as well as of words and parts of words (stems and endings). This cannot be a simple "document." Even to begin to deal with the variety of natural language, the machine's designers had to define and store tens of thousands of commonly used phrases. Each such phrase has several words and spaces, each word several characters, and each character several bits. So the number of memory cells needed to store the bits of this dictionary must be very great indeed. In the machine we are describing, in fact, the dictionary has a capacity of fifty million bits!

How does the machine find a particular phrase in such a comprehensive dictionary? It might look through the dictionary from the beginning, examining each phrase and word, one after another, until it finds one that matches the input typing. But this procedure would involve a catastrophic loss of time. Even at the high speeds of modern computers, such a straightforward sequential search would take too long to find the desired entry. To be useful, the machine must operate at the typical typing speed of fifty words per minute. So, the machine must be able to "skip pages" (just as we do in looking up words in a dictionary) until it reaches the part of the alphabet contained in the first few letters of the input phrase. It examines that page in detail (as we do) until it finds a match. Then it types out the English meaning stored at that point.

So far, so good. But it is too much to ask that the entries in our mechanical dictionary be detailed and numerous enough to match precisely every one of the millions of phrases that may be typed into the machine. Instead, the machine is designed to search in several steps. First, it looks for the exact match of an input phrase containing several words and spaces. If it fails to find this exact match it then automatically tries to find a part of the phrase by looking for successively shorter groups having the same initial letters. It proceeds from a long phrase, then to individual words, and finally to the individual characters in each word.

Since all the characters and punctuation marks are stored individually in the dictionary, the machine will surely find a match at the character level. If it has to go that far to find the match, it types out the English equivalent of the Russian characters and by printing the output in red ink signals that this is a letter-by-letter rendition. By this method of search it can deal with unusual words, such as proper nouns, and any other situation that was not anticipated in compiling the dictionary. This last-resort, letter-by-letter output is a transliteration, not a translation, but it is very useful to the human reader in comprehending the machine's output.

This machine, you will note, is wholly dependent for its performance on two contributions of human intelligence. The first is the dictionary itself. It must be compiled by men who are highly versed in the input and output languages. They must select the phrases, words, and parts of words most likely to be needed in the translation process. Secondly, the designers have equipped the machine with a searching routine that automatically narrows its compass of inquiry. No decision is left to the machine itself; that is, the translation machine operates in the same routine as each new phrase is presented to it.

The basic routine has nine steps: (1) place the code for the input phrase in the input register; (2) turn the "pages" of the dictionary until the part of the alphabet corresponding to the first characters of the input phrase is found; (3) go to the bottom of that page; (4) work backward on that page until a match to the input phrase is found; (5) if no match is found on that page go to the bottom of the preceding page and continue searching backward as necessary to find the match; (6) if no match is found at the phrase level seek shorter phrases, then words, then individual characters, in that order, until a match is found; (7) when the match is found, assemble and type out the English equivalents stored at that point; (8) remove from the input register the phrases, words, or letters that have been translated; and (9) start again with the remaining portion of the phrase (or with the next phrase if the first has been completely translated).

These are the main steps, but there are several others. One is an instruction to break words up into roots or stems, leaving over the inflectional endings, which are looked up. Another is a powerful cross-reference routine, in which the machine inserts prefixes before words, depending on the context of the adjacent words.

We note that the translation machine has received from its designers everything it "needs to know" in the form of its dictionary and its search-and-match routines. Like the antics of the Sphex wasp, its remarkable behavior is explained entirely by its inheritance. The translation machine is only *apparently* intelligent.

A diagram of this machine is shown in Fig. 50. Its

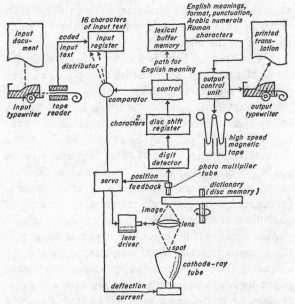

FIG. 50. Diagram of a computer system arranged to translate Russian or Chinese into English. (Courtesy International Business Machines Corporation)

heart is the dictionary, a rotating glass disk on which have been photographed thousands of concentric "tracks." Each track is made up of black segments and transparent segments representing (1) the bits for an input Russian phrase, its words, spaces, and characters, and (2) immediately adjacent on the same track, the bits representing the corresponding output items in English. The input phrases are arranged alphabetically starting with the innermost track and proceeding outward. Each track thus represents a "page" in the dictionary. The first few characters of each phrase or word on that track identify its place in the alphabet.

A tiny spot of light is focused on the disk and the light passes through the disk to a photocell. The photocell generates a series of pulses (ones) for each transparent space on the track, interspersed by empty spaces (zeroes) for each opaque space on the track. The light spot may be moved radially across the disk from track to track, thus "flipping over the pages." When the spot finds the correct track it remains stationary and, as the disk rotates, the bits produced by the photocell represent, in reverse alphabetic succession, all the entries on that track.

Meanwhile, at the input, the typist is feeding in the Russian material to be translated, character by character. Her teletypewriter produces a punched paper tape which embodies the machine code corresponding to the input text. This enters the input register of the computer where the characters are held, sixteen at a time. The input register feeds the bits representing the sixteen characters into a comparison register. Also received by this comparison register is the sequence of bits generated by the photocell examining the dictionary entries.

The comparison register first determines whether the bits representing the first letters of the input phrase are higher (farther down the alphabetic sequence) or lower (farther up that sequence) than the bits read from the dictionary. If higher, the comparison register signals the spot of light (through an intermediate "servomechanism") to move inward. If lower, the spot is moved outward. As the tracks are

234

crossed ("as the pages are skipped") each track is examined momentarily to see if it contains the same initial characters as the input phrase. In a few thousandths of a second, on the average, the correct track is found and the light spot then remains stationary as that track revolves beneath it.

Having found the required track, the machine must now attempt to match the input to the longest phrase stored on that track among the many that have the correct initial letters. The phrases are arranged on the track in order of decreasing length, so the longest phrase automatically is read off first. If a match is found at the longest-phrase level the comparison register signals the control unit to pass the associated bits for the English equivalent toward the output of the machine. If not, the next shorter entry is examined, and so on. Then, if no matching phrase is found, individual words are examined in order of decreasing numbers of letters. Finally, at the end of the sequence, one or two individual characters are found, and a match is achieved on that part. The remaining parts of the phrase are then looked up by skipping tracks until the then-existing initial letters are found, and the process repeats. As each phrase, word, or character is identified successively, it is removed from the input register.

The English equivalents do not go directly to the output teletypewriter. Instead, they are held momentarily in another memory bank (the "lexical buffer") which permits the English parts of the phrase to be assembled according to the rules of English word order before they are released to the output typewriter. This order is determined by "tags" which are appended to the translated word or phrase and reveal its relations to the other forms in the sentence.

Figure 51 shows a typical translation from Russian

¢мировой рекорд скорости 2,260 километров в час был установлен в мае 1958 года на американском самолете ''¢ф-104'', таким образом показанная 31 октября советские летчиком ¢г. ¢к. ¢мосоловым на самолете ''¢е-66'' максимальная скорость превышает мировой рекорд на 244 километра в час.

¢рекордный полет проходил в нижних слоях стратосферы. ¢по правилам ¢международной авиационной федерации (¢ф¢а¢и) летчик должен был дважды на определенном отрезке пути показать максимальную скорость. ¢в одном из заходов он достиг скорости 2,504 километра в час, что в 2.3 раза превышает скорость звука.

World record speed 2,260 kilometres in hour was fixed in May 1958 year on American aircraft ''F-104'', thus showed 31 October Soviet pilot G. K. Mosolovym on aircraft ''E-66'' maximum speed exceed world record on 244 kilometre in hour.

Record flight passed in lower layers stratosphere. By rules International aviation federation (FAI) pilot should have twice on definite section way show maximum speed. In one of approaches it reach speed 2,504 kilometre in hour that in 2.3 times exceed speed sound.

FIG. 51. Typical machine translation from Russian to English.

to English rendered by this machine. Not elegant, but intelligible! Shown in Fig. 52 is a Chinese* translation achieved by a more sophisticated version of this machine. The "tree" of syntax of the Chinese translation, by which the words ("rocket") and

* A typewriter for Chinese ideograms is, in itself, quite an achievement. The Sinowriter typewriter can form 6500 different Chinese characters by striking two keys and adding a number to distinguish among several "look-alike" ideograms. This three-part designation of each character is translated into punched-paper tape code and the machine operates on the bits without "knowing or caring" what the input language "really" is. The interested reader is referred to "Machine Translation of Chinese" by G. W. King and Hsien-Wu Chang, *Scientific American,* June 1963, p. 124. Dr. King headed the team that developed the machine described here. Figure 52 is reproduced from his paper, by permission.

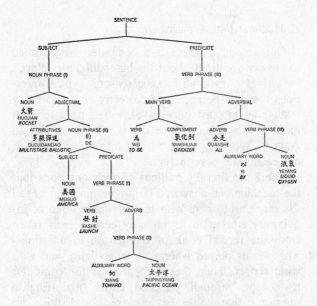

FIG. 52. Syntax tree by which the translation computer assembles Chinese words and phrases into English.

phrases ("Pacific Ocean") were assembled before the output typing, is shown.

A Machine that Answers Questions

Our second example is a computer programmed to answer questions about the baseball games played in a single American League season. Typical questions that can be answered correctly are: Did every team play at least once in each ball park in each month? How many teams did the Yankees play in August? What teams won ten games in July? Where did each team play in June?

There are literally millions of such questions that the machine can answer. The programmers arranged the machine to deal with this particular area of inquiry by storing in its memory certain facts taken from the record book of the season in question—what teams played where, on what dates, and with what scores. Then they arranged for the computer to accept, through punched cards, plain-English questions that could be answered by looking up these records. To keep the logic and memory requirements within bounds they have set certain limits on the form of the questions; only simple interrogatory sentences, without dependent clauses or logical connectives, are allowed. But if the operator is willing to phrase his questions within these limits, he can get fast, correct answers.

To answer questions, the baseball program must perform two tasks. It first must analyze the input question, determine the parts of speech, their meanings and grammatical relationships, rearrange the words and phrases, and draw up a list of required information in a standard format. This list is in effect a long string of bits that represents the meaning of the question. Second, it must pass this string of bits through its memory, looking for matches between the list and the stored data (which is arranged in the same format). This search-and-match routine may be simple, or it may be very complex, depending on the nature of the question. The computer keeps at it until it has drawn from its memory all the data that represent the unknowns in the question. It then types these out as the answers to the question.

The team records are arranged in the memory "data file" in the form of simple equations which represent the known facts. A typical segment of the data file reads:

$$Month = July$$
$$Place = Boston$$
$$Day = 7$$
$$Game\ Serial\ Number = 96$$
$$Team = Red\ Sox;\ Score = 5$$
$$Team = Yankees;\ Score = 3$$

The file, in this format, is arranged in sections, one for each month in the season. Under each month are ten subsections headed by the ten places (ball parks) where the games were played. Under each place are subsubsections for the thirty or thirty-one days in each month. Associated with each day are a game number and the teams and scores of the game played on that day (in the month and place of that section of the file).

The task for the computer, then, is to draw up, from the input question, a list of equations matching this format. Each question offers known facts that set the background of the inquiry, and unknown facts that are to be found in the file as the answer to the question. Suppose the question is, What team won in Boston on July 7? The machine must produce from this question the following "specification list":

$$Month = July$$
$$Place = Boston$$
$$Day = 7$$
$$Game\ Serial\ Number = ?$$
$$Team = ?;\ Score = ?$$
$$Team = ?;\ Score = ?$$

The question marks represent the unknowns that are stated explicitly, or implied, by the question.

By passing the specification list through the data file, the machine can quickly fill in the question marks: 96, Red Sox, 5, Yankees, 3. The machine must now, in a second routine, determine that, since 5 is greater than 3, the Red Sox team was the winner, which is the answer to the question. The machine also prints out the complete specification list and the data for each question mark, to aid the operator in determining whether it has correctly recognized and interpreted all the knowns and unknowns of the question.

The foregoing is a very simple question. The power of the baseball program is better illustrated by a more general question: On how many days in July did ten teams play? To answer by culling the facts from the record book would take a baseball buff some considerable time. The baseball machine deals with it in successive steps. The first causes ev-

ery day in the July section of the data file to be
found, and the number of teams playing on each
day to be counted. Those days are listed when, and
only when, the team count for that day equals ten;
otherwise, the day is passed over. Then, in the final
step, the number of days listed is counted, and the
computer prints out this number as the answer.

A still more difficult question is, Did every team
play at least once in each ball park in each month?
This takes repeated searches in each month-section
of the file to associate all ten teams at least once
with all ball parks. If the association list is complete
the answer Yes is printed; if not, No.

Clever as this matching of specification list to data
file is, the true merit of the baseball program lies in
its ability to derive the specification list from the
question posed. To read the meaning of the question, the computer first compares the words in the
question with entries in a stored dictionary. (This
dictionary is on ordinary magnetic tape, rather than
on a glass disk.) Actually, there are two dictionaries
stored in memory, one for idioms and the other for
individual words. The question is compared first
with entries in the idiom dictionary to see if an idiom
is present. If so, the meaning of the idiom is found
and stored. If not, the question is "passed" through
the word dictionary, and when a word is matched
to a dictionary entry, four items about that word are
found stored at that point: what part of speech it is;
its meaning; whether it is a question word (where,
who, how many, etc.); and whether the word is
cross-referenced to the idiom dictionary. At this
point, the program has "parsed" the question into

its parts of speech and has available the clues of meaning and context.

Next the machine must bracket and rearrange the parts of the sentence by placing square brackets around the nouns and noun phrases, round brackets around the prepositional phrases and the adverbial phrases. A typical input question, Whom did the Red Sox lose to on July 5? becomes, after bracketing and rearranging, "(To [whom]) did [the Red Sox] lose (on [July 5])?" From this arrangement the computer can determine whether the verb forms (unbracketed) are active or passive, which of the noun-phrases is the subject, which the object, etc.

Finally, from the dictionary meanings and cross-references, and the bracketed parts of speech and phrases, the program is ready to draw up the specification list. Many intricate program subroutines are needed here, for example, to bring together a noun and its modifiers, such as $Team_{(winning)}$. The phrase "how many games" must be converted, before its entry on the specification list, to the form $Game_{(number\ of)} = ?$

That an orderly format may be preserved in such circumstances is truly an impressive feat of the programmer's art, but preserved it is. The specification list is drawn up, the data file searched in the manner previously indicated, and the question marks are filled in with the data found in the corresponding locations in the file.

The baseball program always answers a given question in the same way, and with the same search-and-match routines in detail. It does not learn (that is, it does not improve its performance with experience) because it was not designed to learn. It is an exercise in the recognition and matching of meaning, nothing more. But it is an important step toward the goal of free communication between men and machines.

A Machine that Proves Theorems

Our third example is a computer programmed to prove theorems in symbolic logic (Chapter 5). Since the permutations and combinations of logic can become enormously complex (400 trillion truth tables are needed to enumerate all the true-false logical relations among just six statements), solving problems by exhaustive search of all the possibilities is practical only in very simple situations. In nearly every case of practical interest we must use shortcuts (heuristic methods). These do not guarantee a solution, but they offer the possibility that a solution may be found in a reasonable time.

The theorem-proving program described here was devised by Newell, Shaw, and Simon to show how heuristics may be used in a computer. They call it the Logic Theory machine, or "LT" for short. They selected fifty-two theorems from Chapter 2 of *Principia Mathematica* as their test cases. They placed in the computer memory the five axioms and three rules of inference from that book by which the theorems could be proved. They programmed the machine to prove the theorems by searching its memory and manipulating its symbols. The theorems were presented to the machine in order of their appearance in the book. The program was arranged to store each theorem after it was proved by the machine. Each such "proved theorem" could be used later, if necessary, in proving the following theorems.

Our brief exposure to symbolic logic does not permit us to follow the details of the proofs achieved by the machine, but we can get the flavor from three examples. The first of the *Principia's* fifty-two theorems is $(P \rightarrow \bar{P}) \rightarrow \bar{P}$, that is, "(P implies not-P) implies not-P." In ten seconds, the machine found and printed out a four-step proof. The thirty-first theorem is $[P + (Q + R)] \rightarrow [(P + Q) + R]$. The LT program worked twenty-three minutes on this one and finally gave up, reporting that it had exhausted its program resources. The forty-fifth theorem, $\overline{(P + Q)} \rightarrow \bar{P}$, looks simple but is actually a fairly advanced theorem. After twelve minutes, the LT machine found and typed out a five-step proof. The programmers of LT estimate that to prove this forty-fifth theorem by absolute logic (means that would guarantee a proof), the same computer would have to operate for several thousand years!

The LT machine relies on three principal types of heuristic routines, or methods. Each is a self-contained operation that is tried as a subproblem to see if it makes a contribution to the proof. The sequence is shown in the system flow chart in Fig. 53. Having selected the problem, the program tries its methods (described below). It selects a previously proved theorem and tries it on for size. If all the previous theorems fail, it may back up and select a new problem, or it may apply a substitution and then try to find a pertinent axiom or previously proved theorem. It thus works its way through the search for a proof by trial and error. At four points in the program (having failed to find an axiom or a

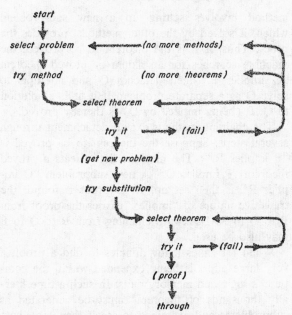

FIG. 53. Flow chart of the logic theory program. (From *Computers and Thought*, edited by Feigenbaum and Feldman, McGraw-Hill Book Company, 1963, by permission)

theorem that contributes to the proof), it goes back to an earlier step and tries again.

The heuristic methods are known as substitution, detachment, and chaining. The substitution method is an attempt to find an axiom or previously proved theorem that can be transformed by substitution of variables (P, Q, R, etc.) or by replacing one logical connective ("or," "implies," "not") by another until an expression matching the theorem to be proved is constructed and recognized. The detachment method involves setting up a new sub-problem which, if solved by the other methods, provides the proof. Thus, if P is the theorem to be proved, the machine searches for an axiom or proved theorem "Q implies P," then detaches Q and attempts to solve Q as a separate problem. If it finds a solution to Q, P (being implied by Q) is thereby proved.

The chaining methods extend detachment through several steps. Suppose the theorem to be proved is "P implies R.": The machine first selects a proved theorem "P implies Q." A new subproblem "Q implies R" is then set up. If its proof is found, the transitive nature of "implies" carries the proof from P to Q to R. Backward chaining from R to Q to P may also be used.

When LT takes many minutes to find a proof, a very large effort is being expended within the computer's logic and memory units. In such a time literally thousands of theorems must be generated as subproblems and examined to see if they contribute to the proof. The effort is assessed in terms of *primitives,* logical operations that are separately carried out as subroutines in the LT program. Proving Theorem 18, for example, required 34,100 such primitive subroutines, each requiring two or three hundredths of a second at better than a million bits per second.

Proofs requiring more primitives than this exhaust the memory capacity of the machine.† The program failed on fourteen of fifty-two tries, partly because of memory limitations, but more generally

† The JOHNNIAC, named after the late John von Neumann, whose work on the stored program concept made him an immortal of computer science.

because the particular heuristic steps of its program overlooked proofs that a rigorously logical (algorithmic) program would surely find, given enough computer capacity and time.

Before leaving LT we must emphasize its purpose: to see whether the heuristics of substitution, detachment, and chaining can be used in a computer to imitate the reasoning processes of the human mind. There is another approach, called *inferential analysis,* which treats the elements of proofs as numbers are treated in calculations. Wang and Gilmore, using such methods, proved all 350 of the logic theorems in *Principia Mathematica* on a 704 computer in less than nine minutes. But they were not seeking to imitate the mind; they were interested in the most efficient use of the computer to find proofs.

Interestingly, Allen Newell does not consider LT to be a program that "learns," at least not under his rather comprehensive definition of learning. We may wish to insist that, according to the usual definition, LT does learn in the sense that it makes use of its experience. It uses theorems not originally placed in its memory, but proved in the course of its work, to solve other problems. True, LT does not generalize on its experience, and generalization is what Dr. Newell finds lacking. To find a program that does generalize, we proceed to our fourth example of machine intelligence.

A Machine that Plays a Game

Our fourth example is the computer system that opened this book, the program designed by Dr. Arthur Samuel to play checkers. We have referred many times to this program and commented on its significance. It is an outstanding (many consider it to be *the* outstanding) accomplishment in programming for artificial intelligence. We need not labor the point, but will describe briefly how the program works.

The object of the game of checkers is to take all the opponent's men or to force the opponent into a position from which he cannot move. There are an unbelievably large number of different moves possible in reaching these end points. According to Dr. Samuel, the complete exploration of every possible path through a checker game would involve perhaps 10^{40} choices of moves. This is so large a number that it is difficult to express in words (in U.S.A. parlance it is ten thousand billions of trillions of quadrillions of moves).

Even if we had a computer capable of considering some 300 million moves per second—and this is faster than the fastest computer presently available—it would take more than a sextillion centuries to explore the game from start to finish for every possible combination of play.

This game, obviously, is one that demands the heuristic approach, whether played by man or machine. The computer program must avoid exhaustive search like the plague. Otherwise, it will take far too long to decide what to do. It must look many moves ahead, but not too many. It must recognize the significant moves and avoid the insignificant ones. In a word, a checkers program designed to beat a champion must do what a champion does—but just a bit faster, wider, or deeper in the strategy of the game.

Human players decide the next move in a checkers game by looking ahead. Usually a player has a choice of several moves that can be made at any point in the game, and he must decide which move will lead, most probably, to victory. One way he can do this is to take up a possible move that "looks good," and imagine that he has made it. He then imagines the board the way his opponent would look at it, and he tries to estimate the response his opponent would make. Depending on his knowledge of his opponent's ability, he will disregard weak responses and thus select from all the possible responses the most probable one. As he presses forward (in imagination) into the third and fourth move ahead, he reaches the limit beyond which he cannot keep all the probabilities, let alone the possibilities, in his head. He then makes his move and "looks ahead" again after his opponent has replied.

Another way of planning a move is to remember a previous game in which the pieces had a similar arrangement. Our player may then recall a sequence of moves that he (or someone else he has observed or read about) has made before. If the remembered sequence was successful he will tend to use it again; if unsuccessful, he will avoid it and seek another move. The best players use both methods, looking ahead along the "probable" lines of play, and remembering classical positions by the hundreds.

Since Dr. Samuel's program has played games of championship skill, it should not surprise us that his program operates along the same lines. The computer looks ahead, listing—in its "imagination"—possible moves, countermoves, counter-countermoves, and so on. From among these possibilities, the computer must choose the most probable moves of its opponent at each "imagined" stage, and interleave these with its own moves. Finally, having thus examined the consequences of the several moves immediately before it, the computer chooses the one that looks most promising and makes it. In this way it plays the game. The program also remembers, and uses to good effect, favorable and unfavorable positions encountered in previous games.

The computer represents the checker board with a 32-bit computer word, one bit for each of the 32 playing squares on the board. Ones represent occupied squares, zeroes empty ones. Four such words are necessary to describe a given board situation to keep track of the white and black pieces, kings, possible jumps, etc. When a piece is moved, the bit for the square moved from becomes a zero, and the bit for the square moved into becomes a one. As each move and countermove is examined, the computer words corresponding to the board position (after the imagined move) are formed and stored away in memory. If the stored words are listed in an orderly sequence it is possible to keep track of all the countermoves that could be made in response to a given move. By organizing the lists in successive echelons the program can go farther, keeping track of each counter-countermove that could be made in response to each countermove, and so on.

By such a process of ordering, organizing, and storing, the machine can construct and memorize *all* the moves and responses that can possibly occur, as far into the future as its memory capacity and the allowable time of play will permit. In this ability the machine is far ahead of the man. The checkers-playing computer can explore as far ahead as twenty

moves; even the best human players can seldom estimate the consequences of a given move (except in
the last stages of a game) farther ahead than four or
five moves.

The process of storing away imagined moves and
countermoves can be represented with a decision
"tree," a simple example of which is shown in Fig.
54. Each branch point on the tree represents the
computer words describing a board position. The
uppermost point represents the board layout of the
actual game; the lower points represent the board
positions after the imagined moves and countermoves have been made. Descending from each
branch point are several lines, each representing a
move that could be made.

The computer must compare several *paths* through
this tree of possible moves. One path represents a
succession of moves most favorable to the computer, interspersed by the most probable moves its
opponent would be likely to make. The uppermost
segment of that path represents the move the computer should (and does) make in the actual game.

The computer works both downward and upward in locating this most favorable path. Starting
with one of the possible first moves, it goes down
one possible path as far as time will permit and
evaluates the resulting board position. Then it con-
siders replacing the last move by a different move.
This process is repeated until a decision can be
reached as to which branch the player would take
at that point. Now the computer must back up the
tree by one level and repeat this process, keeping in
mind that it would be the other player's turn to
move. This process is repeated all the way back up

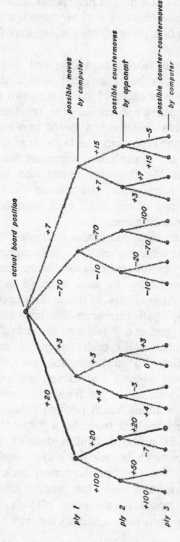

FIG. 54. Simplified version of the decision tree of the checkers-playing computer. (Courtesy A. L. Samuel and the International Business Machines Corporation)

the tree, enabling the computer to evaluate the suitability of the first assumed move.

The computer—fast and patient beast that it is—then explores another path in the tree, the uppermost segment of which is another possible move, and forms the net score of that path. Having thus explored all the available moves, it chooses the one with the highest net score and either signals its choice with lights or prints out that the piece on square such-and-such is to be moved to square so-and-so. This process is practical, of course, only if the size of the tree is kept within manageable limits.

To keep the growth of the tree within bounds, Dr. Samuel has set limits derived from the experience of human players. He calls each horizontal line of branch points a "ply," and he arranged the program to construct (usually) a three-ply tree whenever it has to decide a move. A given branch does not grow beyond the third ply unless "interesting" play develops along that branch; that is, unless a jump or exchange has been made or is offered. When jumps or piece exchanges are evident in any branch, the tree continues to grow along that branch until no more jumps are evident. Then it stops. If jumps continue to be in prospect along a given path, the machine will grow a twenty-ply branch and then stop, arbitrarily, since at that level the machine's memory is in danger of being swamped with words describing all the possible board positions in the tree.

The numbers associated with each line segment in the tree are computed by examination of the computer words representing the two board positions at the branch points at each end of the line segment. By manipulating the four computer words for each of these board positions, the computer breaks up the layout of pieces into small groups and rates each group by various "parameters" derived from the experience of centuries of human play.

In the most advanced form of this program there are thirty-eight such parameters (for example, the "total mobility" parameter equals the number of squares into which the player could move in the normal fashion). By computing these parameter values and subtracting the two values of each associated with the two board positions, the computer forms sixteen numbers descriptive of the two board positions. Each of these is then multiplied by a weighting factor based on the previous experience of the machine, and the sum of the weighted numbers is taken as the "strength" of the line segment in question.

In arriving at the most favorable move, the computer evidently has a large amount of work to do. It does it quickly. Listing the available moves from the given board position, imagining a move and describing the resulting board position, evaluating and weighting the sixteen terms that give the strength of the line segments—all these tasks together are performed in less than two-hundredths of a second on the average. The total time required for the machine to make a move is consistently less than thirty seconds, whereas the time limit in human tournaments is five minutes per move.

Champion Nealey, in playing the computer, consistently took more time than the computer. This lag suggests that if the tournament rules were revised to allow only one minute per move the machine could win much more handily. In fact, Dr. Samuel is inclined to believe that if a substantially larger memory were available, and with a few more years of training time, the program would be unbeatable by man, given five minutes per move.

Thus far we have described how the machine plays the game; that is, how it looks ahead, evaluates the board positions, and works forward and backward to select the move it wants to make. To beat a champion, the machine had to be taken a giant step farther than just playing the game. It had to remember its successes and failures, to play by reference to its past experience, and, finally, to draw inferences about the general features of the game. It is at this latter point that the true power of the program becomes evident.

Actually, Dr. Samuel provided several forms of learning. The first was of a simple type, called "rote learning," which in effect remembered the board positions and used the successful ones again whenever the opportunity was offered. This program never learned to play well. By adding information gleaned at higher ply levels, the scores of the stored board positions were refined and better results were obtained. But championship play did not appear until the general features of the favorable board positions were recognized and catalogued as higher-order abstractions. This is the generalization from past experience that Dr. Newell found lacking in his LT program.

Although the details of the generalization scheme are beyond the scope of this book, the procedure is simply described, and it presages much for the future of artificial intelligence. Two machines were arranged to play each other. One (called Alpha) generalizes on its experience by adjusting the multiplying factors that weight the sixteen numbers previously mentioned. The other machine (Beta) uses fixed values of the weighting factors for the duration of the game. If Alpha wins, the adjusted scoring system used by Alpha is given to Beta, and another game is played. Alpha, again playing by adjusting the weights, may win the second game since Beta uses the fixed (but improved) weights from the preceding game. If Alpha loses, its weight-adjusting scheme is modified by the programmer until it regains the power to win. In this way, the weighting scheme is steadily improved. Observation of the resulting games shows how Alpha is improving. Without being explicitly instructed, it "realizes" many of the basic strategies of the game, such as the benefits of keeping control of the center of the board, avoiding trapped positions at the edges and corners, protecting the king row, and so on.

Note that during this confrontation of two computers, one "teaching" the other, the learning process proceeds within the program without detailed knowledge by the programmer of what is going on. Only in the end result (the actual play) does the nature of the improvement become evident. No wonder that Dr. Samuel calls his program "a very satisfactory device for demonstrating machine learning procedures to the unbelieving."

Finally, we must comment briefly on how the machine acquires an "urge" to win. Suppose the two net scores for two alternative next moves should come out the same. The decision between them must then be made on some basis other than that previously described. Dr. Samuel arranged for this contingency in the first place by keeping a record of the depth within the tree to which the two examinations proceeded. If one net score was derived from a branch proceeding to the sixth ply, while the other went only to, say, the third ply, the six-ply result could be selected for the actual move. But this selection also can be improved. If the next-move scores differed only in ply number, the net score could be changed a small amount depending on the detailed results of the backward search in finding the most favorable path. The machine then could choose the high-ply number if it was losing, the low-ply number if it was winning. In this way the direction toward winning is made evident to the machine and it presses forward decisively. Without this most important factor in the program, early attempts to make the machine learn failed.

CHAPTER 12

CAN MACHINES CREATE?

Oh, many a shaft at random sent
Finds mark the archer never meant!
—SIR WALTER SCOTT

We come now to the final questions of our study. Can machines produce works of art? Can they write literature? Can computers organize the symbols of thought into grand designs of intellectual creation? If they can, man's world may be enriched (or debased!) in ways that can only be imagined.

In the present state of the art, machines can hardly be said to be creative. True, a start has been made. Computers have produced art forms, but these are thus far of no great significance. At best, today's computers can only assist man in creative work. So our questions must be addressed to the future. Can a machine ever, conceivably, create an original and noteworthy composition—one equal in quality to a masterpiece of human creation?

To attack this question, let us examine the symbols, patterns, and processes used in a creative composition and relate these to corresponding symbols, patterns, and processes of computers. Computers can manipulate all manner of symbols, including the symbols of art. They can produce patterns of these symbols in unending variety. They can recognize likenesses and differences in these patterns. If a programmer can devise criteria of artistic excellence, in some field of creative endeavor, he can adjust his computer to search for and select patterns that meet these criteria and to print them out for critical appraisal.

If, as in Turing's test, the critics must decide (or guess) whether the work in question was composed by man or machine, an error in their judgment may be taken as evidence that the machine can imitate man in that particular field of artistic endeavor. (Again, we permit intelligent machines to be judged by their works, not their methods.) To the best of my knowledge, no computer system has ever been subjected to this test. As we shall see, the Illiac computer has been programmed to compose music. But the most that musicologists will admit is that the output is "interesting"—hardly of human quality.

We shall spend some time with the Illiac program for composing music, because it illustrates a technique not previously mentioned in this book, the deliberate introduction of *chance* in computer programs. The music-writing machine is programmed to select musical notes *at random,* fast and furiously. The sequences of notes are subjected to several tests, based on the established rules of musical composition and the style of a given school of composition. If a sequence meets these tests, and if it links up properly with the preceding and following patterns, the computer prints it out, measure by measure.

Otherwise, it rejects the sequence and tests another randomly generated pattern.

Evidently any computer programmed for artistic composition must, in the first place, be able to deal with the symbols of the art. Music has a relatively small number of symbols, and this convenience makes it a suitable candidate for experimentation. Secondly, the computer is constrained to arrange these symbols within the rules of composition of that art. In music well-defined sets of rules may be used. Thirdly, the computer must be free to vary the patterns in ways not prohibited by the rules. This is the same freedom that gives the human composer the scope he needs to improvise, select, and polish, until he finds the forms that satisfy his creative urge.

The artistic machine has no creative urge, but it nevertheless can improvise (using random processes), select (by testing patterns against criteria written in its program), and polish (by reference to higher-order criteria), until the constraints of its program are satisfied. Moreover, the computer can draw on its superhuman resources of speed and endurance. In a few hours it can search for and test, accept or reject, artistic patterns that would occupy a man for a lifetime.

Most important, the computer may be programmed with fewer constraints than the human artist has. Every artist is the prisoner of his culture, just as every computer is the prisoner of its program. Only a few great artists* in each generation

* One wonders whether Stravinsky's *Le Sacre du Printemps,* which caused a major riot when it was first heard, would have been more calmly received if it had been composed by a computer.

break through these constraints. The computer program, given sufficient hours to race through the broad fields of art, may provide breakthroughs on a radically shorter time scale.

Design and Chance in Art

To illustrate the function of chance in art, let us examine two "mechanical" art forms. The first, the snowflake, comes from nature. The second, von Foerster's cubes, was invented by a computer scientist to show how "selection rules" imposed on a disordered situation can produce an ordered result resembling modern sculpture.

As we know, no two snowflakes have ever been found alike in detail, but all have features in common. There must, therefore, be a thread of *order* in the structure of a snowflake that persists through the random *disorder* of its growth. The forces between atoms permit only one arrangement of the ice molecule; that is, the atoms of oxygen and hydrogen are packed together in the form of tetrahedrons. When these tetrahedral molecules come together to form an elementary ice crystal, the intermolecular forces produce a six-sided figure.

When the conditions of crystal growth are extraordinarily favorable, this shape persists and large hexagonal crystals of ice may be formed (hailstones sometimes have this shape). But such conditions seldom obtain. When a snowflake is formed, its elementary crystals come together in an endless variety of ways, depending on the random changes in its environment (e.g., temperature and vapor pressure) by which its growth is affected. The selective forces between atoms and molecules nevertheless are always present, and these affect the end result: every snowflake has six-sided symmetry (Fig. 55).

FIG. 55. Six-sided symmetry of a snowflake derives from the tetrahedral shape of ice molecules, but the unending variety of their shapes depends on chance. (From *Crystals and Crystal Growing*, Science Study Series)

Here we have a combination of order, imposed by physical forces in the fine structure of every snowflake, and disorder imposed on a particular snowflake by the random events and sequences of its growth. The beauty of snowflakes resides in their symmetry and their variety. The symmetry comes from order, the variety from disorder.

Von Foerster's art form is produced from several dozen hollow cubes of iron, shaken up in a box. So long as each cube has no attraction or repulsion for its neighbors, the cubes, when shaken and the box opened, are found to be in a wholly disordered state (Fig. 56). By chance, some may rest on others, as shown at the right of the figure. But chance is so overwhelmingly in charge of this game that no ordered pattern emerges from the pile of cubes.

Next, suggests Dr. von Foerster, let us *magnetize*

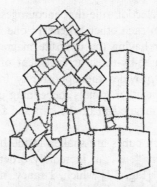

FIG. 56. Von Foerster's Cubes. Shaking the cubes produces this disordered array when there are no selective forces acting between the cubes. (From *Self-Organizing Systems,* edited by Yovits and Cameron, Pergamon Press, 1960, by permission)

each face of the cube independently† so that the lines of magnetic force proceed *outward* on some faces, *inward* on the others. There are just ten different ways of magnetizing each cube in this way. Suppose we first consider cubes whose lines of force proceed outward on all six faces. Then every cube repels every other, no matter what its orientation to its neighbors. When such cubes are shaken, the pile in the box may be more dispersed than when the cubes were unmagnetized, but the pattern still has no discernible order. The mere fact of *uniform* magnetism has not produced an ordered arrangement.

Now suppose we adopt a more selective scheme of magnetizing the faces and see to it that three coterminous faces of each cube are magnetized in the outward direction, the remaining faces inward. Now

† This is possible because the cubes are hollow.

we have a selection rule that encourages neighboring cubes to join each other, whenever one face encounters another having the opposite magnetism. Moreover, the three-by-three arrangement of the magnetized faces provides the opportunity for *groups* of cubes to join other groups, depending on the direction of the magnetism of the exposed faces of each group.

When such cubes are shaken in the box, says Dr. von Foerster, ". . . an incredibly ordered structure will emerge [Fig. 57] which, I fancy, may pass the

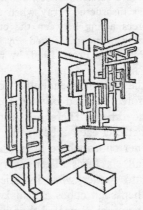

FIG. 57. Selectively magnetized cubes, when shaken, "organize" themselves into an array resembling modern sculpture. (From *Self-Organizing Systems,* by permission)

grade to be displayed in an exhibition of surrealistic art." We note that, if the jury of the exhibition does not like this first sample, vigorous shaking will produce another, and another, and another.

The close analogy between the structure of the three-by-three magnetized cubes and the snowflake is evident. Both have simple basic elements (tetrahedrons and cubes); both have selective forces between elements; both are subject to random processing; both are members of a class of patterns exhibiting at the same time symmetry and variety. Both are works of art.

The world is full of such examples. Artists and composers deliberately choose geometric patterns as the basis of their compositions and then elaborate on them until a "satisfying" result is achieved. The Cubist school of art is an example. So are the Mirror Fugues of Johann Sebastian Bach, who chose geometric patterns of notes, and then inverted them from measure to measure, and voice against voice, as they would appear when viewed in a mirror. These fugues are not mere curiosities. Had they been, Bach would not have released them to his publisher. The process of writing certain sequences of the notes depended on the mirror mechanism, but the final judgment of merit was the judgment of genius.

Will a computer, having produced a fugue one of these days, print out: "This is one of my best works"?

Not soon.

Illiac and Its Music

In 1955, Hiller and Isaacson began a series of experiments in computer-composed music at the University of Illinois. By 1956 they had accumulated enough computer output to assemble the *Illiac Suite*

265

for String Quartet, which subsequently was published.‡ This suite consists of four "Experiments." "Experiment I" generated melodies and simple four-part harmony; "Experiment II" added variety by employing fourteen stylistic rules, typical of such sixteenth-century composers as Palestrina. "Experiment III" introduced variety of rhythm and other musical dynamics combined with occasional dissonance, and produced music resembling the style of the twentieth century. "Experiment IV" composed without reference to any historical style, purely by mathematical concepts, including reference to a table of probabilities to set the intervals between notes. This attack produced an atonal type of music, which sounds like the "modern" music of Experiment III, although it was based on a wholly different philosophy of programming.

Like the snowflake and von Foerster's sculpture, the Illiac music is based on a few elementary symbols, selected at random, with selective "forces" (composition rules) to link them in "acceptable" arrangements. The symbols of the first experiment were the fifteen white-key notes which comprise two octaves of the C-major scale; no black-key sharps or flats were admitted. The integers 0 to 14 inclusive were assigned to these notes, and the computer was arranged to generate these integers at random. Some of the sequences of notes were melodic, but the vast majority were not. To select the melodic ones, additional program instructions were added to screen the sequences of integers by reference to the

‡ Those who may wish to study or perform this work may obtain the score from Theodore Presser Company, Bryn Mawr, Pennsylvania.

rules of sixteenth-century composition. If the melodic line from one integer to the next (from note to note) met these tests, the integer was stored in the machine's memory, and the sequence was built up until the melodic line completed itself by returning to the note C. Then the completed sequence was printed out and transcribed (by hand) to standard musical notation.

Not every sequence of notes could be concluded successfully as a melody, and to avoid endless searching, the machine was arranged to give up after fifty unsuccessful tries to find a next "melodic" note. It then erased the stored melodic line and started over again from another, randomly chosen first note. Proceeding thus for an hour, Illiac composed several hundred melodies of from three to fourteen notes each.

The next step in Experiment I was to arrange the machine to compose two melodies and to select pairs of notes that met simple rules of two-part harmony. The selection was based on four additional computer instructions which screened out dissonances between the two notes in a given pair and permitted the consonant pairs to be stored. Finally, the program was extended to compose four melodic lines at once, with four notes constrained to be in harmony. Thus, a composition suitable for trial by a string quartet was produced. In proceeding from two to four voices in harmony, the machine had to give up and erase its trials more and more often, but, as Dr. Hiller said, "The machine still composed copiously."

Figure 58 is a block diagram of the music-writing computer. At the left is the random number genera-

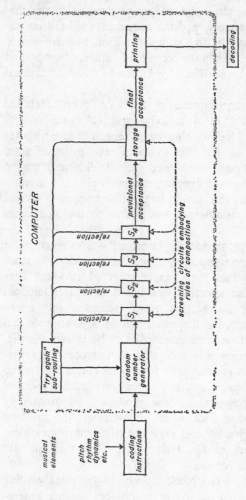

FIG. 58. Diagram of the Illiac Computer programmed to compose music. (From "Computer Music," by L. A. Hiller, *Scientific American*, December 1959, p. 111, by permission)

tor that produced the successive integers representing the notes. Each integer was passed in succession through a series of screening circuits which embodied the rules of composition. The integer had to pass through four such screenings before it was accepted provisionally as a part of the melodic line. If it failed to pass, the screening circuits signaled the "try-again subroutine," and a new note was generated, at random, and the screening repeated for it. If fifty failures occurred in a row, the erase function came into play and the process began anew.

Figure 59 shows a selection from "Experiment I"

FIG. 59. Portion of the Illiac Suite for String Quartet (above), compared with human music of the same style (Palestrina, sixteenth century. By permission of Theodore Presser Company).

of the *Illiac Suite,* compared with a portion of Palestrina's *Adoramus Te Christe.* Those who can read (or play) these examples will note that the computer music is comparatively monotonous, because the program of "Experiment I" provided no variation in rhythm, whereas Palestrina was under no such restriction. The third "experiment" repaired this omission and introduced more variety in the selection of melody and harmony, advancing the style from the sixteenth to the twentieth century. In "Experiment III," for example, 4/8 time was selected and the eighth-note taken as the smallest rhythmic unit. The notes were coded in binary fashion in groups of four, thus making sixteen different rhythmic sequences. Each was assigned an integer from 0 to 15 inclusive, and these integers were randomly generated in the manner of the first "experiment." To avoid irregular sequences, additional redundancy rules were incorporated in the screening program. Finally, by similar methods, such dynamics as *forte* and *crescendo* and instructions like *legato, tremolo,* and *pizzicato* were introduced. By 1962, Hiller and Baker had reported§ an advanced program for all eighty-eight notes of the chromatic scale, incorporating four different "orders" of syncopation.

A fascinating development in this work is the analysis by computer of (human) musical masterworks, to discover their mathematical structure. The computer findings are then embodied in the selection rules of the screening circuits to assist composition

§ See Hiller, "Computer Music," *Scientific American,* December 1959, p. 109, and Hiller and Baker, "Computer Music," Chapter 18 in *Computer Applications in the Behavioral Sciences,* p. 424 (Prentice-Hall, 1962).

in that particular style. Little of moment has resulted from this musical training of a computer by a computer, but the concept is fascinating, and strongly reminiscent of Computer Alpha's instructing Computer Beta how to play a better game of checkers.

Originality: Chance versus Purpose

This brief review of the Illiac music reveals an important characteristic of its scheme of composition. The program is essentially imitative, not original. True, the compositions produced are different in detail from anything previously written. But their general form was constrained (in the first three "experiments") by selection rules written by human programmers in imitation of human music. Only in "Experiment IV" was the program released entirely to chance, probability, and mathematical forms.

Whatever originality appears in the Illiac music rests ultimately on random searching, which is, of course, the antithesis of artistic purpose. The keen awareness of a task to be performed, so evident in human creative work, is absent in the computer. If this distinction between random search and creative purpose is fundamental, we must conclude that machines can be creative only in the narrow sense of imitation. But if some way can be found to give machines the direction of purpose (however "unconscious" of that purpose they must remain), then original works satisfying an artistic drive may be created. An elementary form of purpose—to win— was given to the checkers-playing computer, you will recall, by a subtle but essential detail in its program (Chapter 11). The computer chose one of two otherwise equally desirable moves, depending on whether it was ahead of or behind its opponent at the time.

Newell and Simon recently have attacked the problem of computer purpose in another way, in a program they call the General Problem Solver (GPS for short). It enables a computer to find the means to an end, by setting up goals that can be reached by transforming, reducing, and operating on the given problem situation until it takes the form of a solution. GPS bears a close relation to the Logic Theory program of the same authors, described in Chapter 11, and it has been tested on the same material (proofs in symbolic logic). In a test of GPS, a college student who had not previously been exposed to symbolic logic was told the symbols for "and," "or," "implies," and "not" and twelve rules for substituting and transforming these relations. He was then asked to prove, if he could, that $(R \rightarrow \bar{P}) \cdot (\bar{R} \rightarrow Q)$ could be reduced to $(\overline{\bar{Q} \cdot P})$. He was asked to talk aloud as he wrestled with the problem, and a tape recording was made of what he said. Understandably, he soon got stuck, and the last words on the tape were, "I'm just sort of lost for a second."

The same problem was then put on a computer programmed for GPS, and a detailed print out was made of the steps taken. These were then compared, item for item, with the recording of the human effort. An astonishing similarity was discovered, as well as several significant discrepancies. The man often considered several possible avenues simultaneously, whereas the computer worked sequentially. Moreover, the man had a keen sense of what was internal to the problem, as against the external situation in which he found himself. This awareness was not, of course, available to the computer. But the GPS programmers are confident that these discrepancies can be removed, provided the subject matter is not too complicated. They go further and say that the techniques of GPS "reveal with great clarity that the free behavior of a reasonably intelligent human can be understood as the product of a complex but finite and determinate set of laws."

Does this conviction imply that a computer, capable of dealing with this same complex set of laws, could display the same free behavior? Newell and his co-workers thus focus attention on relative complexity, rather than difference in principle, between the intellectual attainments of men and machines.

We may well be impressed that a computer can compose anything, albeit in the comparatively simple situation of musical symbolism, and in imitative fashion. But we are asking bigger questions: Can a computer be original on a grand scale? Can it found a new school of composition? Can it devise, on its own, a coherent point of view, and impose that view on its compositions?

The nature of such an accomplishment can be explored by proceeding to another creative field, literature. Here the scope of the symbols and the range of their combination are vastly greater than those of music. The range of concepts and relationships used, for example, in composing poetry (which must take account of the sounds as well as the meanings of words, and must depart from normal modes of expression) may forever transcend the bounds of computer science.

Certainly, no presently conceivable computer can

criticize poetry, let alone compose it. The nature of the computer output necessary to deal with poetry is illustrated in an imagined "conversation" (published by M. V. Wilkes in 1953) between Turing's Examiner and a machine:

Examiner: Do you know the sonnet that begins, "Shall I compare thee to a summer's day?"?

Machine: Yes.

Examiner: Would not "a spring day" do as well or better?

Machine: It wouldn't scan.

Examiner: How about "a winter's day"; that would scan all right.

Machine: Yes, but nobody wants to be compared to a winter's day.

Examiner: Would you say that Mr. Pickwick reminds you of Christmas?

Machine: In a way.

Examiner: Yet Christmas is a winter's day, and I do not think Mr. Pickwick would mind the comparison.

Machine: I don't think you're serious. By a winter's day, one means a typical winter's day, rather than a special one like Christmas.

A machine conversing in this fashion would be thinking as a poet thinks. With the enormous reserves of memory, association of ideas, and imagination implied by this conversation, such a computer could, almost certainly, create original literature. Dr. Wilkes did not pose this imagined conversation to imply that such a machine will ever exist. His purpose was to focus attention on the workings of the creative human brain, and to ask: "Is the brain a machine?"

Is the Brain a Machine?

The question Can Machines Create? (on a grand original scale) cannot be answered with any certainty today. The answer can only be a guess. The direction of our guess depends in a large measure on our beliefs. If we accept the proposition that the brain *is* a machine, then in principle—if not in practice—we can build a machine like it. But if we wish to insist that the creative brain is not a machine—that it operates in a vitalistic, non-materialistic basis, not definable in mechanistic terms—then we cannot hope to build a machine like it.

Newell, Shaw, and Simon are explicit in their conviction that free human behavior is based on a complex but determinate set of laws. In their view, if we are to produce, mechanically, creations of human quality, we must discover these laws, and we must devise a machine and a program complex enough to embody them and their implications. This may be a larger order than we can imagine ever being filled. But it provides the best guess we have: Machines can conceivably create on a grand scale if the creative methods of the brain can be reduced to computer science. The computer need not imitate the brain in every detail of its creative power, but, in all probability, it must use heuristics; that is, it must adopt shortcuts similar in principle to those used by the brain to bring the order of creation out of the chaos of its environment.

In the end, we must concede that every computer

is a part of nature; it must operate according to a limited set of natural laws. Given the power to encompass *enough* natural law, we may guess that it can attain all the conclusions implied in natural law —even to the writing of poetry.

What are the prospects that such a powerful computer and program can ever be devised? A timid answer is easy. The brain and nervous system of man are so utterly complex that no conceivable machine that will ever be built and programmed by techniques now known or even guessed at can hope to equal it. But a bolder answer is also at hand: We can conceive that structures and programs very much less complicated than those of the brain, but well beyond present attainments, can create by imitating only those functions of the brain actually used in human creation. This is a far less ambitous objective than imitating the brain in all its functions.

We recall from Chapter 9 that there are more than a trillion electrical connections among the neurons of the human animal, and that subtle chemical and thermal forces, as well as electrical ones, are at work. To reproduce all these functions in a machine is now impossible, and it may forever remain so. Even if so monumental a construction should become possible, the chances are that it would not be attempted. It would serve no useful purpose.

One may argue safely that most of man's nervous capacity is not used in the processes of thought. An estimate places the storage capacity of the human memory at not less than a million billion bits. Much of this capacity is tied up with the internal economy of bodily functions, apart from conscious thought, and additional reserves are applied to unconscious actions, like "remembering" how to keep our balance as we walk. The intellectual computer needs no such resources. Its bodily functions and its actions are simple in comparison, and all its memory can be concentrated on the program of imitating thought.

A key issue thus emerges. What part of the human system is used in its programs for thought? It may be a trivially small portion of the total. If so, the prospect of providing similar capacity in a computer system is not so forbidding. One bit of evidence is at hand: the elementary processes of perception and reaction in mankind proceed so slowly that, in the waking hours of a whole lifetime, the human mind can process, consciously, no more than 50 billion bits of information. If all these bits were stored in the human memory they would take up less than 1/20,000th of its total capacity. The input perceptions and output reactions of a computer can match those of a human lifetime in a few hours. Again, the million-times speed advantage of the computer cannot be gainsaid.

The trade-off of computer speed against human complexity offers, as we noted in Chapter 9, an opportunity to place machines on an equal footing with the brain, for certain defined tasks. It may never be worthwhile to produce and program a machine equal in versatility to the brain. But it will certainly be worthwhile to do so, when and as we have the resources, for important particular tasks, those that man does so poorly or so slowly that the costs of the machine and its program are justified.

In ten years, the speed and memory capacity of computers have increased more than tenfold. In the same period, the concept of machine-aided coding has arisen, and the power of compiler languages grows, visibly, month by month. In the next several decades, these trends will continue. Each advance in speed and capacity and each new insight into the functions of language will open new doors. Before the next century arrives, our question will not be, "Can machines create?" The operative question will be, "What tasks of machine creation are worth the cost?"

The Long Look

We guess, then, that creative power equal to man's, in certain fields, will be available, and economically justified, in computer systems within the lifetime of the younger readers of this book. Beyond that, we ask our final question: Will intelligent machines ever reach intellectual attainments beyond the limits of the human brain?

It is easy to dismiss this question with an abrupt No! Man, who must design and program the machine, cannot possibly provide a structure and a scheme he cannot himself conceive. This may be the correct answer. But those who have studied how man has reached, through eons of time, his present intellectual power can see new vistas ahead as evolution proceeds.

The argument proceeds from the conviction, not contradicted by physiological or psychological evidence to date, that the classes of problems capable of being formulated and solved by the human intelligence are limited by the structure of the brain. This structure has evolved from lower forms through the processes of evolution. At several key points in history, a new set of abstractions has come within man's compass. Perhaps the most significant in recent history (on a geological time scale) are the abstractions of human language, which came into being within the last half million years, more or less. If a new (and by definition now unthinkable) set of abstractions is in store for the human race, mankind may well expect to wait a similar period, if Nature is left to her own devices.

When a new order of abstraction is added to an intelligent machine, however, the process proceeds on a different time scale. The process depends, in the first place, on the available technology, such as methods of producing, connecting, and actuating larger arrays of logic elements and memory cells. It depends, secondly and perhaps even more importantly, on the available rationale of programming, which orients the problems to the machine. At present, neither the technology nor the rationale gives us any indication of abstract power beyond that of the brain.

Future computer techniques may always fall short, but not by definition. Just as we can visualize the concept of infinity (that is, can think generally of a number larger than any particular number we have ever put into words), so can we visualize a machine and program whose hierarchy of abstractions contains one echelon above the highest echelon of natural thought. Further, we may conceive that this extra echelon need not be "thought out" by man (who, by definition, does not possess the mental equipment for the task). It *might* be produced by

279

extrapolation from previous designs. In this sense, intelligent machines may forge into the unknown.

If and when technical methods and programming techniques permit such an extrapolation, we can be sure that the attempt will be made. It will not matter that man cannot conceive, by definition, of what processes would be employed by the machine in this higher-than-human set of abstractions. It will be sufficient that the machine, dropping down to the level at which it can communicate with man, can reveal verifiable truths obtainable in no other way.

Such speculations, in the view of many computer experts, are at best idle, at worst irresponsible. But if we wish to share the excitement that permeates research in artificial intelligence today, we must not avoid the heady thought that man may indeed take hold of his own intellectual evolution, by devising tools and techniques that nature might otherwise withhold for thousands of centuries.

A FORTRAN PROGRAM FOR COMPUTING π

The FORTRAN statements for the π computation described in Chapter 8 are given below with their literal meanings and explanatory remarks. In reading the program the following FORTRAN conventions should be kept in mind:

(1) Only capital letters are used.

(2) The symbol * means "multiplied by."

(3) The symbol ** means "to the exponent."

(4) Parentheses are used (as in algebra) to enclose operations that are to be performed individually. For example, $4./(2.*N-1)$ is interpreted by the computer to mean:

    (a) Form the quantity 2N.

    (b) Subtract one from the result.

    (c) Divide the difference into 4.

(5) Statements beginning with IF call for a test of the sign of the quantity inside the parentheses. Depending on whether the sign is minus, zero, or plus, the computer will transfer control to the respective statement number associated with each of these conditions in that order. For example, the statement IF $(N-101)$ 3, 6, 6 is interpreted to mean: If the quantity $N-101$ is negative, go to statement 3; if zero, go to statement 6; if positive, go to statement 6.

The program is as follows (note that the statement numbers are identified in Fig. 46):

Statement Number	FORTRAN Statement	Meaning to Programmer
1	DIMENSION TERM(100)	The programmer's name "TERM" represents a one-dimensional array of 100 memory positions. Each position in the array is available to the programmer through the subscript N. This array will contain the computed quantities for the 100 terms.
2	N = 1	Store a decimal one in memory location N. N will be used both as a subscript and in computing the value of the 100 terms.
3	TERM(N) = (−1**(N + 1)) * (4./(2.*N − 1.))	This defines the signed value of the quantity TERM(N). For the first time, N = 1; the term is calculated with this value. The result is stored in the first position of the array TERM. The second time the calculation is made with N = 2. The result is stored in the second position of the array, and so on.
4	N = N + 1	Add 1 to the contents of location N and store the result in the same location, N.

5   IF (N−101) 3, 6, 6
    If the result of subtracting 101 from the contents of N is negative, return to statement 3. Proceed to the following statement (6) on a zero or positive result.

6   N = 1
    Restore the contents of memory location N to 1.

7   SUM98 = SUM98 + TERM(N)
    Add to the contents of memory location SUM98 (initially zero) the contents of the current position of the array. Store the sum in location SUM98.

8   PRINT 28, N, TERM(N)
    (This statement may be deleted if printing is to be omitted.)
    This statement causes the printing of the current position of the array (subscript N) and the contents of that position (the computed value of the current term). The number 28 means the printing format of this statement is controlled by Statement 28.

9   N = N + 1
    Add 1 to the contents of location N and store in location N.

10 IF (N−99) 7, 11, 11
    If the result of subtracting 99 from N is negative, return to Statement 7. If zero or positive, go to next statement (11).

Statement Number	FORTRAN Statement	Meaning to Programmer
11	SUM99 = SUM98 + TERM(N)	Add the sum stored at SUM98 to the 99th term (since N is equal to 99). Store the result in memory location SUM99.
12	SUM100 = SUM99 + TERM(N+1)	Add the 99-term sum statement to the 100th term. (N+1 is equal to 100.) Store the result in memory location SUM100.
13	IF (SUM98 − 3.141592) 14, 23, 23	If the 98-term sum is less than the given value of π, go to the next statement (14). Otherwise go to Statement 23, for the error condition.
14	IF (SUM99 − 3.141592) 23, 23, 15	If the 99-term sum is greater than the given value of π go to the following statement (15). Otherwise go to Statement 23, for the error condition.
15	IF (SUM100 − 3.141592) 16, 23, 23	If the 100-term sum is less than the given value of π go to the following statement (16). Otherwise go to Statement 23, for the error condition.

16   AV89 = (SUM98 + SUM99)/2.

Add the 98-term sum (stored in location SUM98) to the 99-term sum (stored in location SUM99). Divide the sum by 2 and store the result in location AV89.

17   AV90 = (SUM99 + SUM100)/2.

Add the 99-term sum (stored at SUM99) to the 100-term sum (stored at SUM-100). Divide the sum by 2 and store the result in location AV90.

18   COMANS = (AV89 + AV90/2.

Add the contents of location AV89 to the contents of location AV90. Divide the sum by 2 and store the result in location COMANS (for "*computed answer*"). This statement forms the average of the two averages previously stored by Statements 16 and 17.

19   IF (COMANS − 3.1415920) 21, 191, 191

If the result of subtracting 3.1415920 from the computed answer is zero or positive, go to the following statement (191). Otherwise go to Statement 21. This statement causes PROBLEM UN-SOLVED to be printed if COMANS is less than 3.141592.

Statement Number	FORTRAN Statement	Meaning to Programmer
191	IF (COMANS − 3.1415930) 20, 21, 21	This statement causes PROBLEM UN-SOLVED to be printed if COMANS is 3.141593 or greater. Otherwise PROB-LEM SOLVED is printed by transfer to Statement 20.
20	PRINT 26	This statement causes the printing of PROBLEM SOLVED. The format of this statement is contained in Statement Number 26.
201	GO TO 22	This statement is shown on the LOGIC CHART of Fig. 46 as an arrow to box 22. It causes the computer to skip over Statement 21 and go to State-ment 22.
21	PRINT 27, COMANS	This statement causes the printing of PROBLEM UNSOLVED and the (wrong) computed value of π. Used in connection with Statements 19 and 191. The manner in which the print-ing occurs is defined in Statement 27.

22	STOP	This statement causes the computer to terminate its execution of this problem.
23	PRINT 25	This statement causes the printing of ERROR IN MAGNITUDE OF SUM. Control is transferred to this statement by Statements 13, or 14, or 15. The format is given in Statement 25.
24	GO TO 22	Return to Statement 22 to terminate any further processing of this problem. (If the error message of Statement 23 occurs, there are one or more logic errors in the program.)
25	FORMAT (25H ERROR IN MAGNITUDE OF SUM)	This statement contains the 25 alphabetic characters and spaces of the message that will appear on the printer. Used in connection with Statement 23.
26	FORMAT (14H PROBLEM SOLVED)	This message contains the 14 characters and spaces of the message that will appear on the printer. Used in conjunction with Statement 20.

Statement Number	FORTRAN Statement	Meaning to Programmer
27	FORMAT (16H PROBLEM UNSOLVED, E13.6)	This statement contains the 16 characters and spaces of the message to be printed, plus the format for the (wrong) computed value of π. Used in connection with Statement 21. E13.6 causes a floating point number to be printed in the form $+N.DDD-DDDE+XX$ where the first plus sign represents the sign of the number. It will be blank if the number is positive. The N and D's represent the integer and six decimal places of the number. The last four numbers $(E+XX)$ represent the number of times the number will be multiplied by ten. A plus number means move the decimal point to the right XX places. Move the decimal point left on minus. For example; the number $-4.123400E+02$ means -4.123400 times 10 to the 2nd power or $-412.34\ldots$

28   FORMAT (13, E13.6)   This statement, used with Statement 8,
                             provides the format for printing the 3
                             characters of the value of location N
                             (subscript) and the format for printing
                             the floating point value for the term
                             contained in that position of the array.

29   END   This is the last statement of the pro-
                             gram. It tells the FORTRAN compiler
                             that there are no more statements to
                             compile in this program.

FURTHER READING

Adler, Irving. *Thinking Machines*. New York: Signet Science Library (Paperback) (1962).

Borko, Harold, ed. *Computer Applications in the Behavioral Sciences*. Englewood Cliffs, New Jersey: Prentice-Hall (1962).

Bowden, B. V., ed. *Faster Than Thought*. London: Sir Isaac Pitman & Sons (1953).

Dantzig, Tobias. *Number, The Language of Science*. Garden City, New York: Doubleday & Company (Anchor Books) (1956).

Feigenbaum, Edward A. and Feldman, Julian, eds. *Computers and Thought*. New York: McGraw-Hill Book Company (1964).

Flores, Ivan. *Computer Logic: The Functional Design of Digital Computers*. Englewood Cliffs, New Jersey: Prentice-Hall (1960).

Galambos, Robert. *Nerves and Muscles*. Garden City, New York: Doubleday & Company (Science Study Series) (1962).

Greenberger, Martin, ed. *Management and the Computer of the Future*. New York: McGraw-Hill Book Company (1962).

Pfeiffer, John. *The Human Brain*. New York: Pyramid Publications (Paperback) (1962).

Pólya, G. *How to Solve It*. Garden City, New York: Doubleday & Company (Anchor Books) (1957).

Weiner, Norbert. *Cybernetics, Control and Communication in the Animal and the Machine*. New York: John Wiley & Sons (1948).

Wooldridge, D. E. *The Machinery of the Brain*. New York: McGraw-Hill Book Company (1963).

INDEX

Abbreviations: for computers, 73; language, 66

Accumulator registers, 150–51

Accuracy of computers, 5

Adaptive intelligence, tests for, 218–21

Addend bit, 106, 109

Adder truth tables, 118

Addition: in binary arithmetic, 29–31; switching circuits for, 37–40

Adoramus Te Christe (Palestrina), 270

Algebra of classes (*see* Classes)

Algebraic problems, computer operations for, 47–59

All-or-none logic, 94–104

Analysis by brain, 181–82. *See also* Human intelligence; Reasoning

"And" relation. *See* Conjunction

Animal intelligence: apparent, 215–16; real, 217

Apparent intelligence: in animals, 215–16; artificial, 217–18; of computers, 232; real versus, 212–15

Archimedes, 13–15, 93

Arithmetic. *See* Binary numbers; Computer arithmetic

Arithmetic unit, 46–47

Artificial intelligence: apparent, 217–18; arguments against, 210; definition of, 213, 225–26; experience in, 2–6; features of, 213–14; future of, 278–80; heuristics and, 93–94; human intelligence compared with, 205–8; learning in, 2–6; programming of, 214–15

Artistic composition: chance and design in, 261–65; programming for, 260

Asynchronous computer, 137

Auditory cortex, 185

Auditory nerve, 181

Augend bit, 106, 109

Babbage, Charles, 207 *n*

Bach, Johann Sebastian, 265

Back-to-back circuit, 113

Baseball-question computer, 238–43

Binary adder circuits, 119

Binary numbers, 22–44; addition of, 29–31; charac-

SCIENCE STUDY SERIES